Contents

Sounding out letters

Look at the pictures. Say the words. Sound out the beginning letters.

| | a | aaa (not 'ay') |
| ant | | |

| | g | guh (not 'jee') |
| goat | | |

| | b | b-b-b (not 'bee') |
| bat | | |

| | h | hhh (not 'aitch') |
| hat | | |

| | c | ck (not 'see') |
| cat | | |

| | i | ih (not 'eye') |
| igloo | | |

| | d | duh (not 'dee') |
| dog | | |

| | j | juh (not 'jay') |
| jar | | |

| | e | eh (not 'ee') |
| egg | | |

| | k | ck (not 'kay') |
| key | | |

| | f | fff (not 'eff') |
| fish | | |

| | l | lll (not 'ell') |
| log | | |

Note for parent: This activity helps your child to practise phonemes. Each letter is next to the sound it makes rather than its name.

mug	m	mmm (not 'em')
nut	n	nnn (not 'en')
octopus	o	o (not 'oh')
pen	p	puh (not 'pee')
queen	q	qu (not 'kew')
red	r	rrr (not 'aar')
sun	s	sss (not 'ess')

ten	t	tuh (not 'tee')
umbrella	u	uh (not 'you')
van	v	vvv (not 'vee')
web	w	wh (not 'double-you')
box	x	ks (not 'ex')
yo-yo	y	yuh (not 'why')
zebra	z	zzz (not 'zed')

Beginning sounds

Say the name of each picture. Match the things that begin with the same sound.

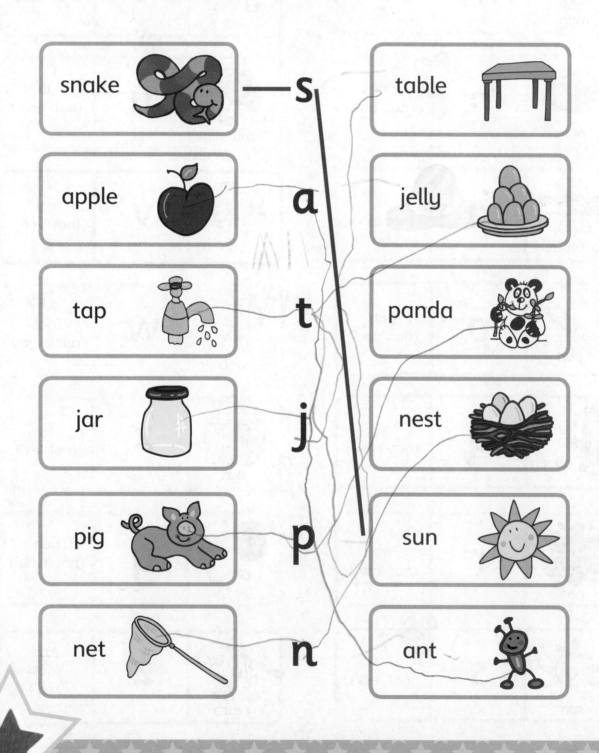

snake	table
apple	jelly
tap	panda
jar	nest
pig	sun
net	ant

s
a
t
j
p
n

Note for parent: This activity gives your child practice in listening for beginning sounds. Encourage your child to say the sound of the letter, not its name – **s** is 'sss', not 'ess'.

cat

elephant

hat

fish

rat

moon

dog

c

e

h

f

r

m

d

fox

monkey

duck

cup

egg

rabbit

hand

More beginning sounds

Say the name of each picture. Circle the pictures in each row that have the same beginning sound.

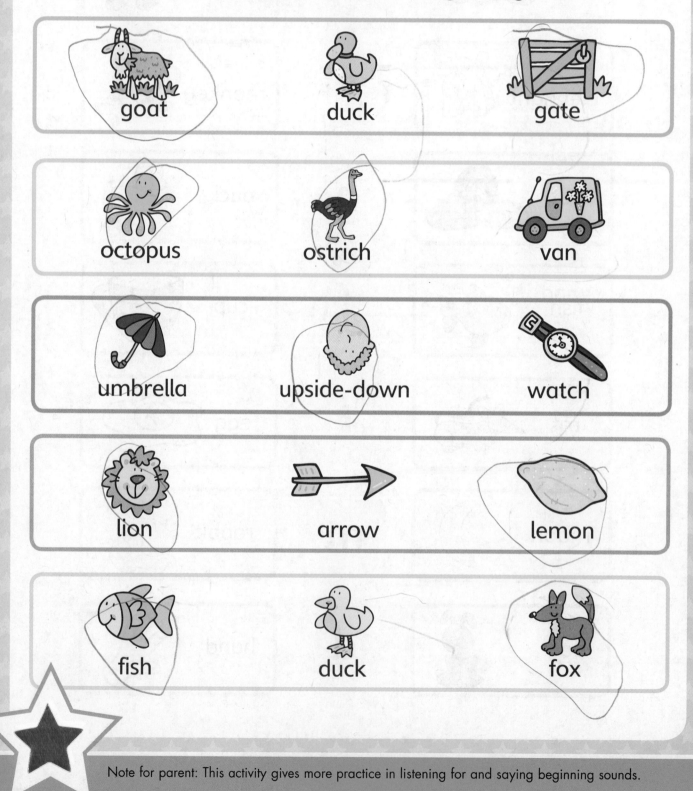

goat

duck

gate

octopus

ostrich

van

umbrella

upside-down

watch

lion

arrow

lemon

fish

duck

fox

Note for parent: This activity gives more practice in listening for and saying beginning sounds.

juggler

elephant

jelly

zebra

zip

teddy

window

lion

witch

violin

van

butterfly

yo-yo

apple

yellow

cow

cap

rocket

Words that rhyme

Say the name of the picture on each card. Match the white cards with words that rhyme on coloured cards and then colour them the same.

mouse

car

bat

key

boat

frog

house

star

cat

tree

coat

dog

Match the rhymes

Say the name of the animal on each envelope.
Circle the picture that rhymes with it.

Note for parent: Encourage your child to explore more rhyming words. Make up silly sentences
about each animal. For example: "Mr Rat sat on a fat cat."

Make new words

Make new words by changing the beginning sounds. Use the letters in the box and the pictures to help you.

h   f   r   c   s   m

tap
bun
pen
hat
rug
van

_c_ap
_s_un
_h_en
_r_at
_m_ug
_f_an

Join each letter to the things in the picture that begin with the same sound.

f   s   c   b

Make up a story about what is happening in the picture.

Note for parent: This activity helps your child to identify beginning sounds. Encourage your child to tell you a story about what is happening in the picture.

13

Draw the words

Read the descriptions.
Draw the animals.

One day we went for a walk
and we saw...

...a big, buzzing,
busy bee

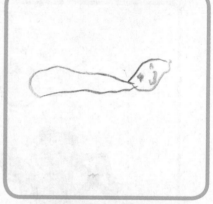

...a spotty, slippery,
slithering snake

...a pair of pretty,
pink pigs

...and four funny,
floppy fish.

Note for parent: This activity practises beginning sounds word comprehension. Have fun describing
other animals your child might have seen.

Find the words

Find the words in the puzzle. Colour them in.

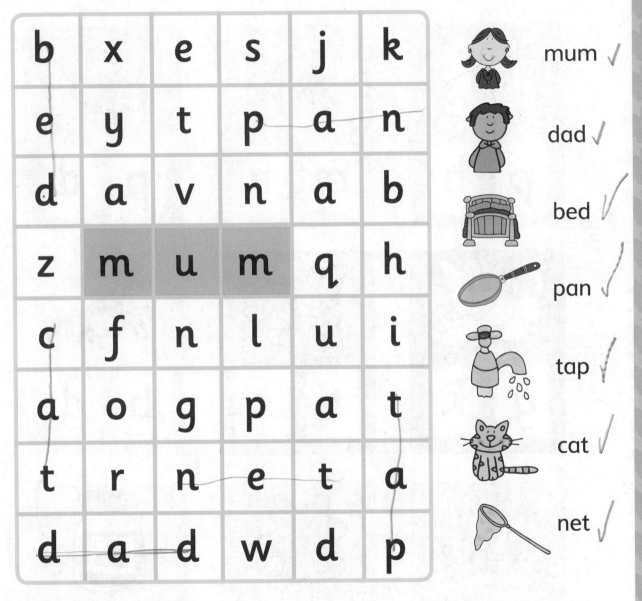

b	x	e	s	j	k
e	y	t	p	a	n
d	a	v	n	a	b
z	m	u	m	q	h
c	f	n	l	u	i
a	o	g	p	a	t
t	r	n	e	t	a
d	a	d	w	d	p

mum ✓

dad ✓

bed ✓

pan ✓

tap ✓

cat ✓

net ✓

Write the words.

Note for parent: This activity gives your child practice in CVC words – consonant, vowel, consonant. Some words go across and some go down.

Sounds at the end

Say the name of each picture. Colour the letter that makes the sound at the end of the word.

p b

m n

p d

g k

t c

b d

x n

m k

n m

Note for parent: This activity helps your child to listen for the final sound in a word. Encourage your child to think of other words that end in the same sounds.

More than one

Add an s sound at the end of a word when there is more than one thing.

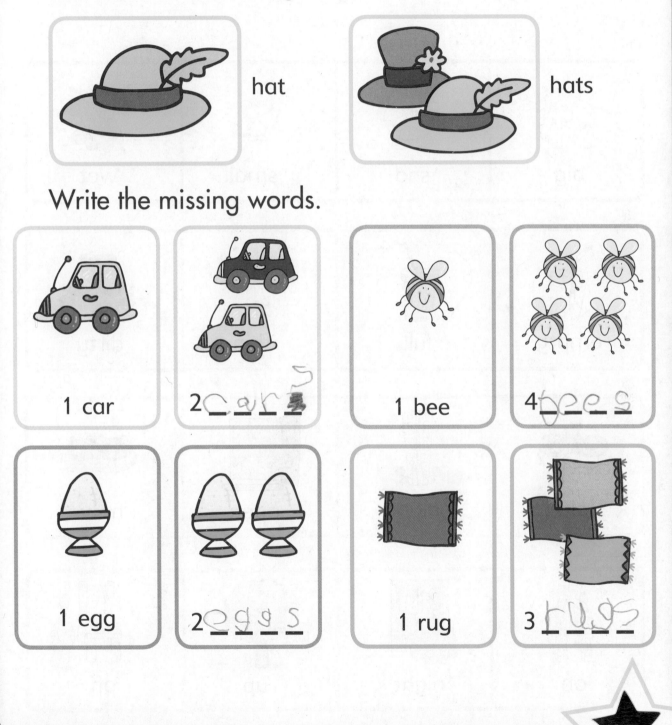

hat

hats

Write the missing words.

1 car

2 cars

1 bee

4 bees

1 egg

2 eggs

1 rug

3 rugs

Note for parent: This activity helps your child to understand plurals (more than one), starting with simple plurals, where you just add **s**.

17

Opposites

Read the words in each row. Circle the word that has the opposite meaning to the first word.

big   sad   small   wet

empty   full   thin   dirty

old   high   open   new

on   night   up   off

What happens next?

Draw what you think happens next.

Note for parent: This activity helps your child to develop the idea of telling a simple story with a beginning, middle and ending.

19

ch and sh sounds

Say the word for each picture. Draw lines to join each picture to the correct beginning sound.

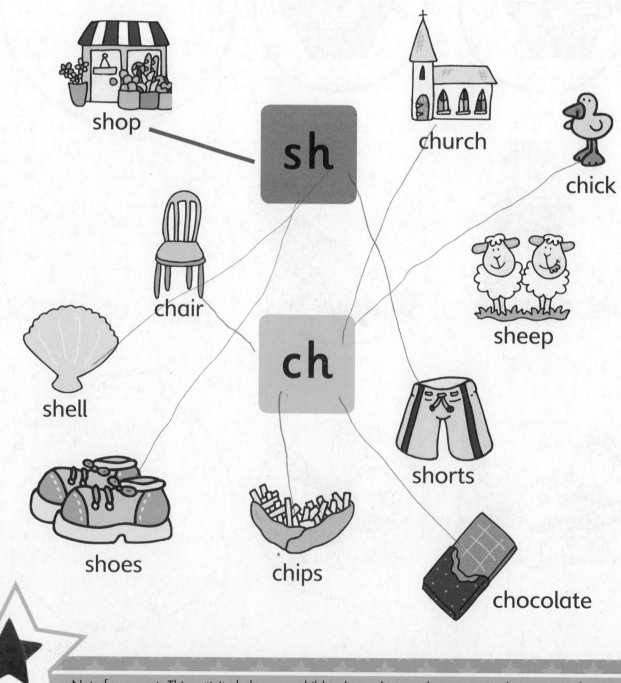

shop

church

chick

sh

chair

sheep

shell

ch

shorts

shoes

chips

chocolate

Note for parent: This activity helps your child to learn that two letters can make one sound.
It gives them practice in distinguishing between **ch** and **sh** sounds.

Use the pictures and words to complete the puzzle. All the words begin with the **th** sound.

thumb

thermometer

throne

thimble

thin

three

Middle sounds

Look at each picture and say the word. Circle the sound that is in the middle. Write the sound to finish the word.

	a i	p_e_n
	e u	b_u_s
	o e	l_o_g
	a e	w_e_b
	e a	c_a_t
	i e	n_e_t

More middle sounds

Say the word in the basket.
Colour the balloons with the
same middle sound as the
word in the basket.

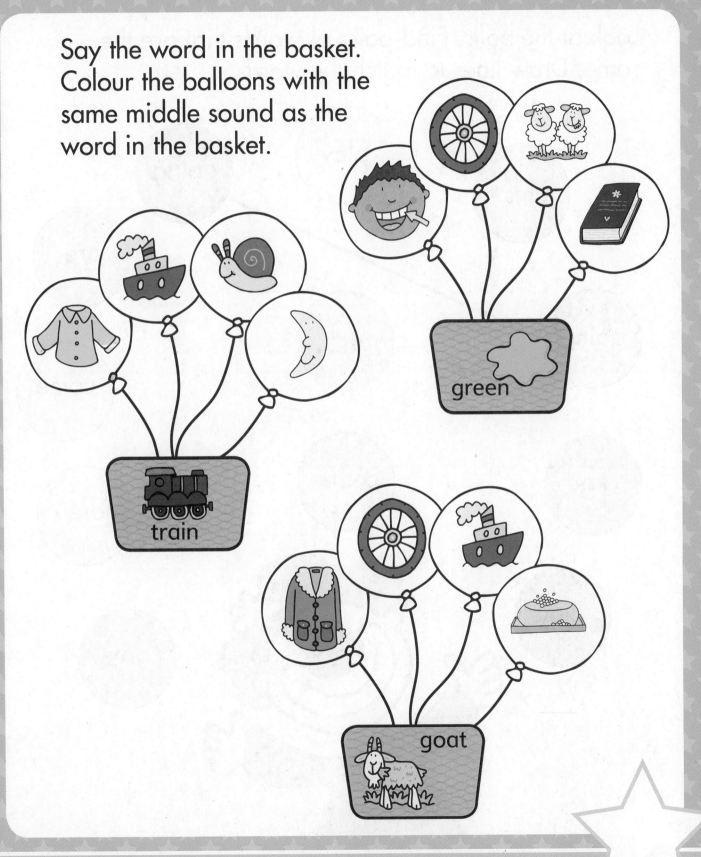

Note for parent: This activity gives your child more practice in recognizing middle sounds and understanding that two letters together can make one sound.

23

Catch the ball

Look at the balls. Find pairs of words that are the same. Draw lines to match the words.

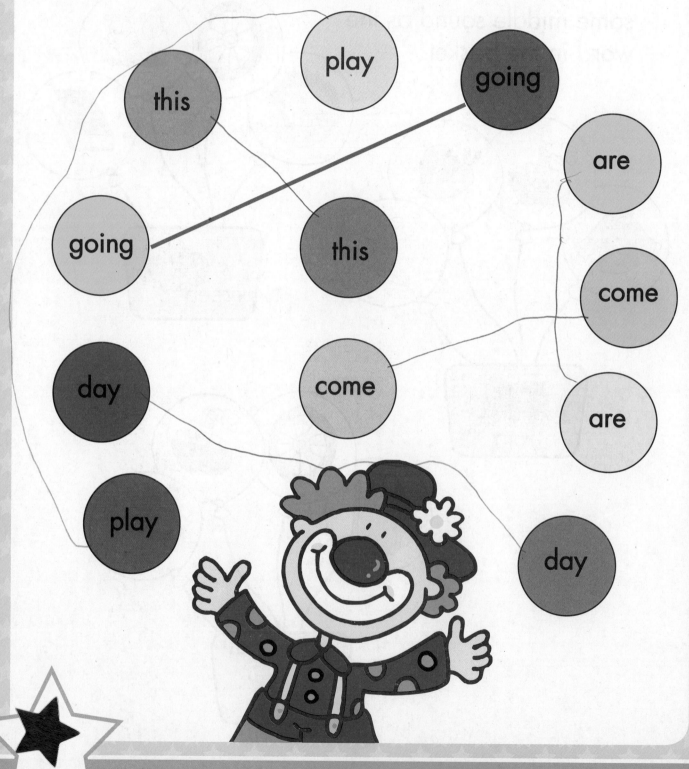

Three-letter words

Read the words. Draw a circle around the word that matches each picture.

cat
cot

pin
pen

fun
fan

dog
dig

man
mum

day
dad

peg
pig

cup
cap

Snakes and ladders

Draw lines to match the same words on each ladder.

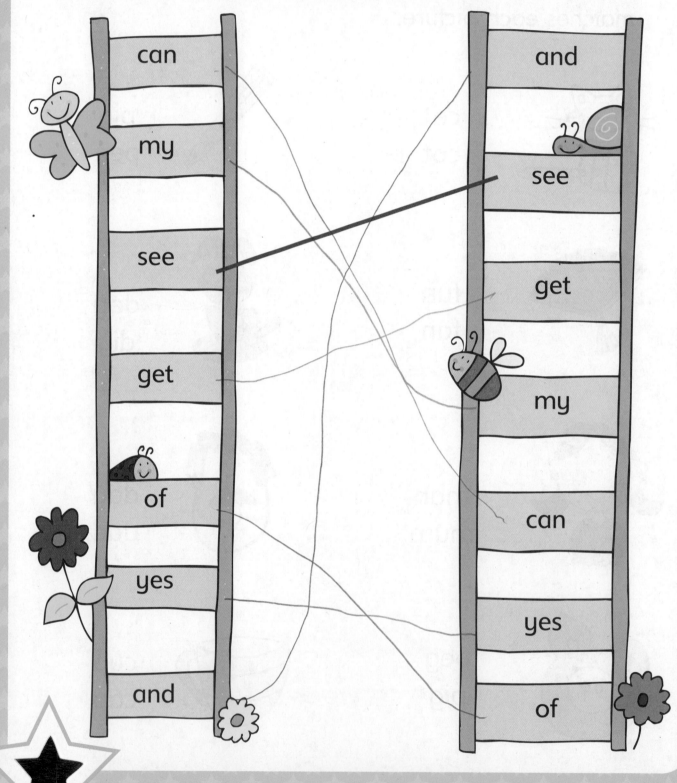

Note for parent: This activity gives more practice in reading high-frequency words.

Draw lines to match the same words on each snake.

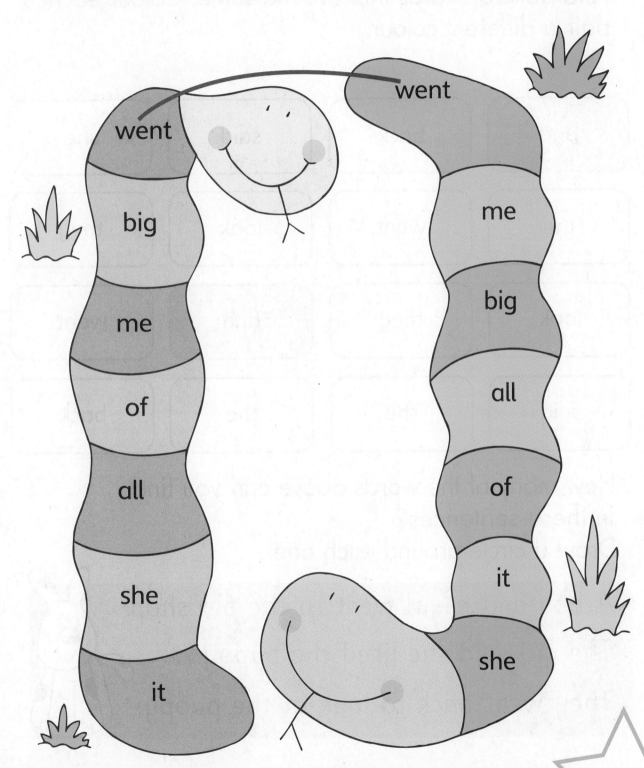

Colour the words

Find pairs of words that are the same. Colour each pair a different colour.

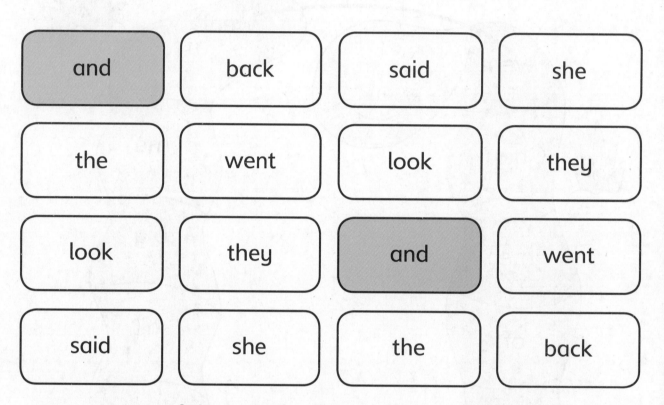

and	back	said	she
the	went	look	they
look	they	and	went
said	she	the	back

How many of the words above can you find in these sentences?
Draw a circle around each one.

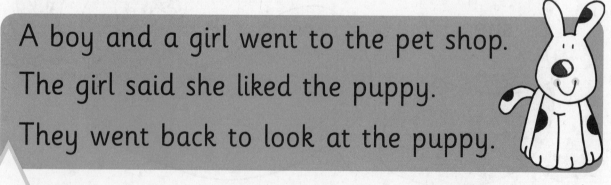

A boy and a girl went to the pet shop.

The girl said she liked the puppy.

They went back to look at the puppy.

Note for parent: This activity gives your child practice with common high-frequency words. Explain that words at the start of a sentence begin with a capital letter.

Find the little words in the big words. Circle the little words.

the   mother

her   father

an   grandad

to   octopus

in   window

on   crayon

Note for parent: Looking for little words in bigger words helps your child with word recognition and spelling. Find other little words in these words.

Read the words in the tree. Join each word to the right apple.

Note for parent: This activity gives more practice in high-frequency words.

Read the words in the rocket. Join each word to the right star.

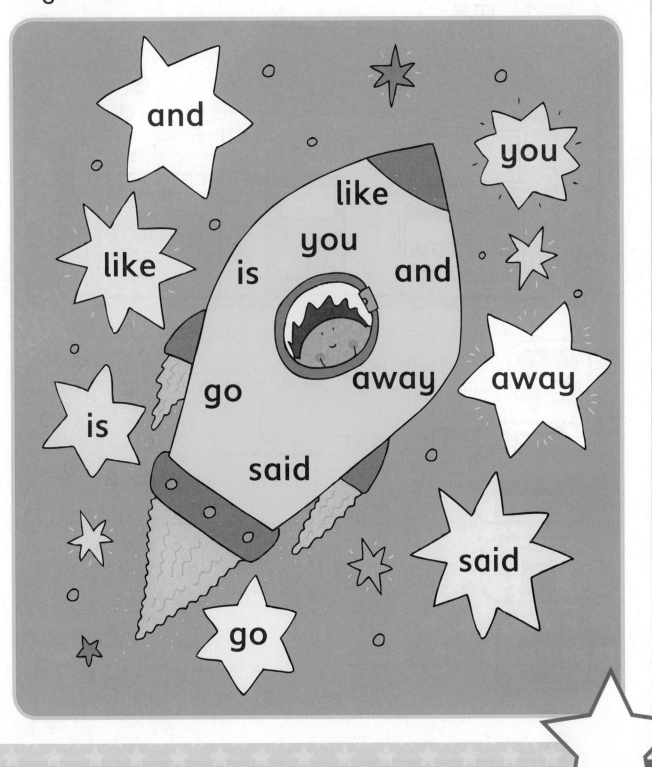

House words

Look at the picture. Write in the missing words.

roof

house

window

door

garage

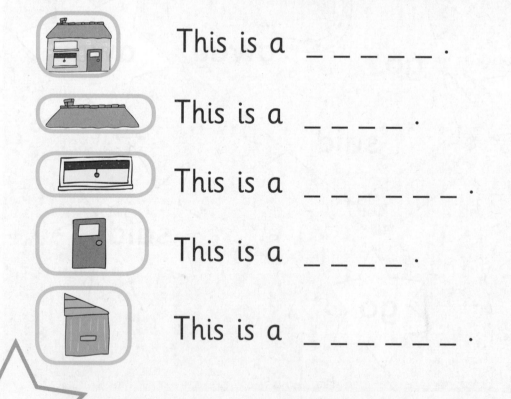

This is a _ _ _ _ _ .

This is a _ _ _ _ .

This is a _ _ _ _ _ _ .

This is a _ _ _ _ .

This is a _ _ _ _ _ _ .

Note for parent: You can also help your child to write your house number on the door in the picture.

Missing words

Use the words in the boxes to complete the sentences. Write them in place.

| is | a | cat |

This is my _____.

It _____ white.

It has _____ long tail.

| can | dog | big |

This is a _____.

It _____ bark.

It is _____.

Sentences

Use the pictures and words to complete the sentences.

coat   door   desk   chair

dinosaur

bed

net

The coat is on the back of the d _ _ _.
The n _ _ is under the bed.
The d _ _ _ _ _ _ _ is on the bed.
The chair is near the d _ _ _.

Capital letters

Look at these names. They all begin with a capital letter.

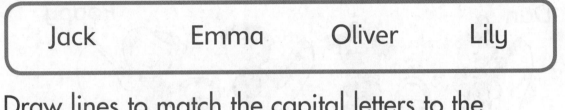

Jack   Emma   Oliver   Lily

Draw lines to match the capital letters to the small letters.

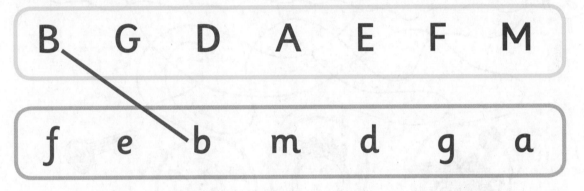

B   G   D   A   E   F   M

f   e   b   m   d   g   a

Colour all the capital letters in the puzzle.

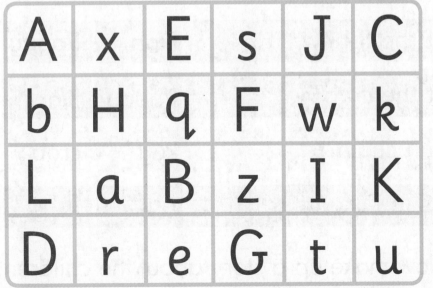

A	x	E	s	J	C
b	H	q	F	w	k
L	a	B	z	I	K
D	r	e	G	t	u

Note for parent: Tell your child that names always begin with a capital letter. Together, write out the names of people in your family.

35

Tell the story

Trace the fishing lines to see what each person has caught.

Dan   Mia   Ali   Poppy

Circle the correct answer.

Who caught the fish?	Dan	Poppy	Mia
Who caught the crab?	Poppy	Dan	Ali
What did Dan catch?	key	crab	ring
What would you like to catch?	ring	fish	crab

Now make up a story about the children.

Note for parent: This activity encourages your child to look carefully. Read the questions to your child.

Odd one out

Say the words in each group. Listen to the sounds.
Circle the odd one out in each group.

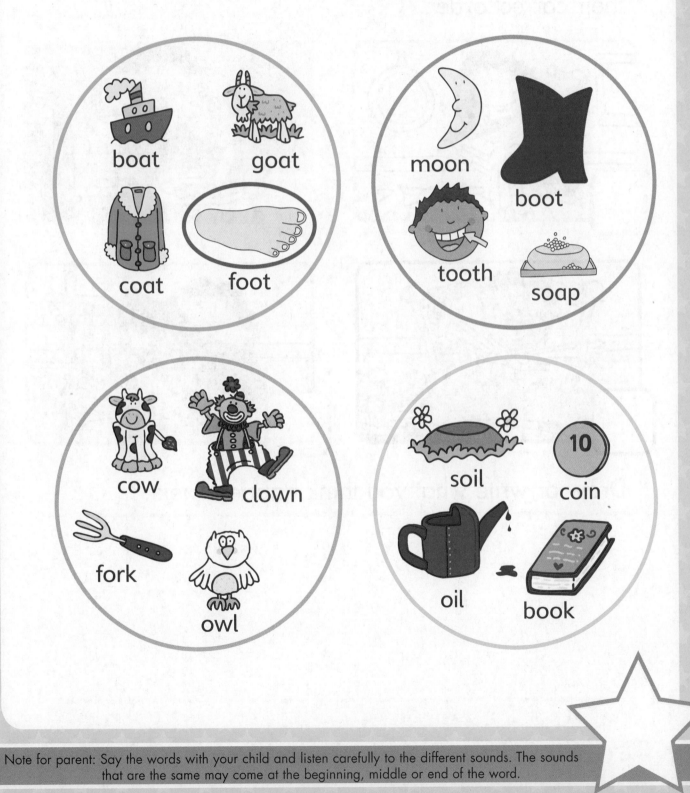

boat

goat

coat

foot

moon

boot

tooth

soap

cow

clown

fork

owl

soil

10 coin

oil

book

Note for parent: Say the words with your child and listen carefully to the different sounds. The sounds that are the same may come at the beginning, middle or end of the word.

37

Make a story

Look at the four pictures to see what is happening. Write the numbers 1 to 4 in the boxes to show their correct order.

Draw or write what you think happens next.

Note for parent: This activity gives your child practice in story sequencing. Talk about what is happening in each picture. Work out the order of the story.

Tricky words

Look at the shapes of these words. Write the words in the matching boxes.

little they what some like
when said have was all do

little

Note for parent: This activity gives your child practice in learning some tricky high-frequency words.
The shape of a word can help your child to recognize it when reading.

39

Join the dots

Join the dots in the right order. Begin with **a**.

| a | b | c | d | e | f | g | h | i | j | k |

What can you see?

Note for parent: Practise saying the alphabet with your child.

What is it?

Join the dots in the right order. Begin with l.

l m n o p q r s t u v w x y z

What can you see?

Strokes

Trace the dotted patterns.
Start at the red dot and follow the arrow.

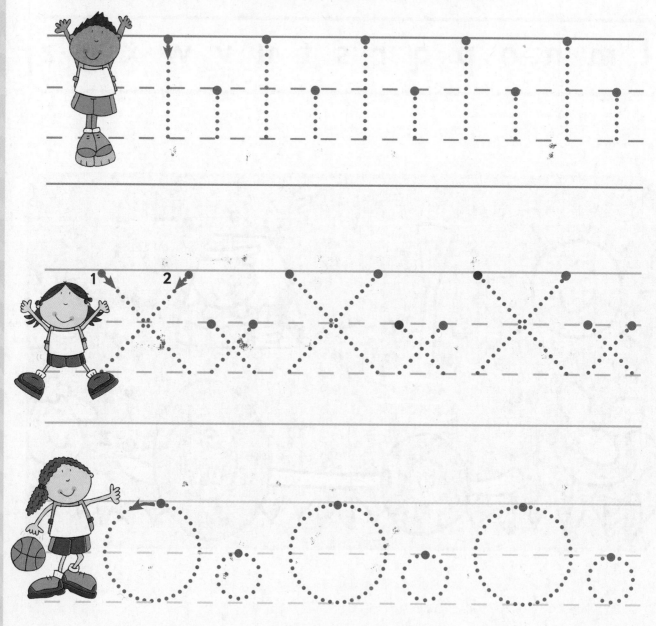

Note for parent: This will help your child to practise drawing within the guidelines and keeping their strokes a regular size.

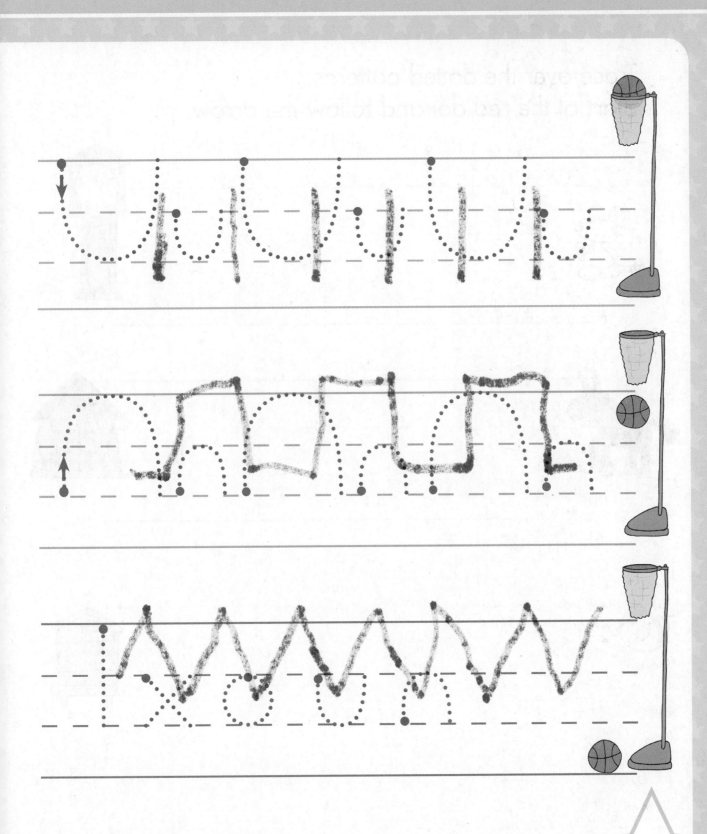

Patterns left to right

Trace over the dotted patterns.
Start at the red dot and follow the arrow.

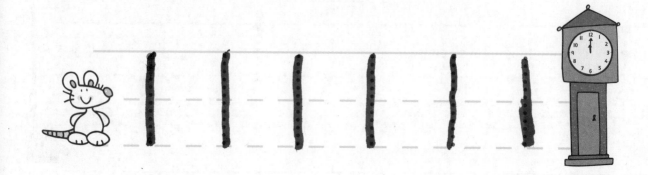

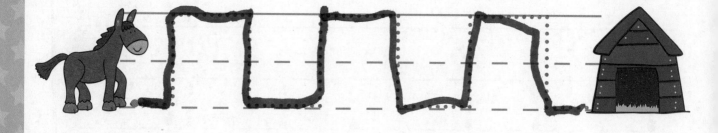

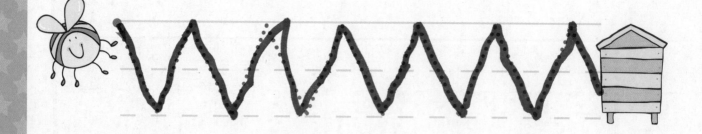

Note for Parent: This will help your child to practise pencil control. The movements will prepare your child for making good letter shapes.

uuuu

mmmmmm

eeeee

Trace the letters with your finger. Then trace over the dotted lines to write the letters. Start at the red dot and follow the arrow.

cat

The letter **c** goes down and round.

cake

car

Note for parent: The letters in this activity all begin at the top and move down in an anticlockwise direction.

The letter **o** goes down, around and joins up at the start.

orange

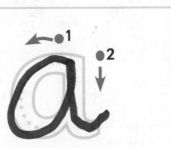

owl

The letter **a** goes down, around and back down again.

ant

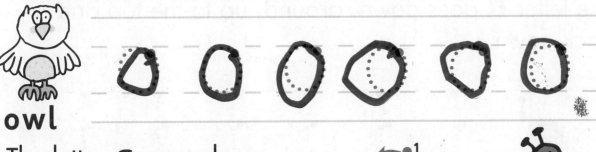

apple

Writing d, g and q

Trace the letters with your finger. Then trace over the dotted lines to write the letters. Start at the red dot.

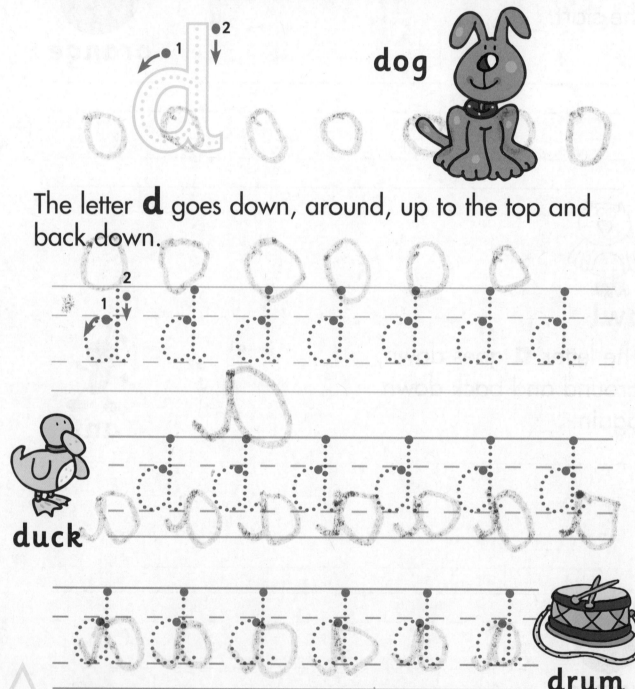

dog

The letter **d** goes down, around, up to the top and back down.

duck

drum

Note for parent: These letters give practice in adding upwards and downwards strokes. Show your child how the tails on the **g** and **q** are different.

The letter **g** goes down, around and down below the line with a curly tail.

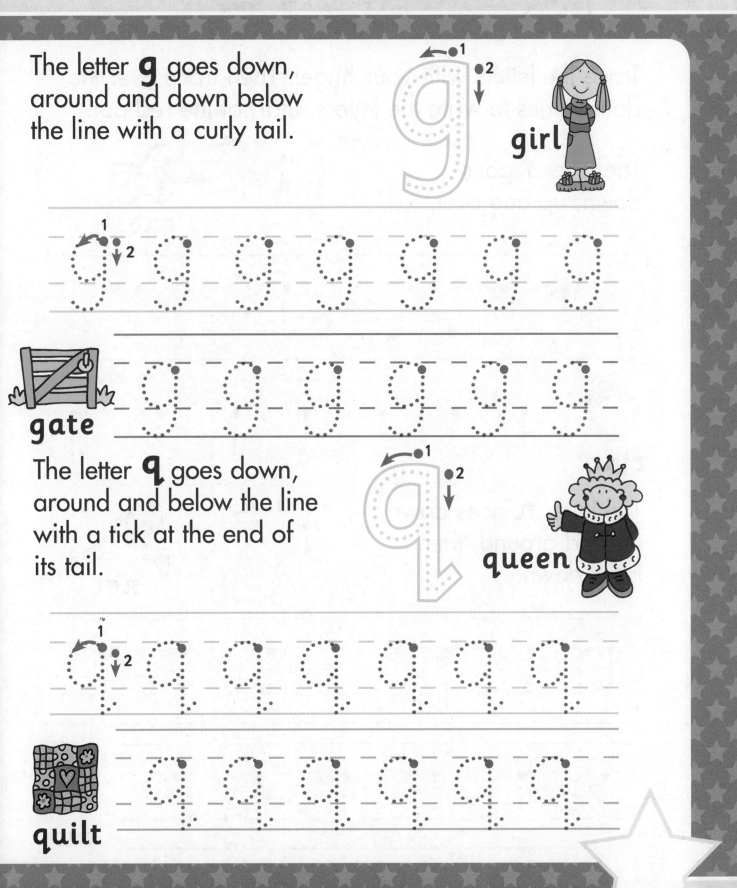

girl

gate

The letter **q** goes down, around and below the line with a tick at the end of its tail.

queen

quilt

Trace the letters with your finger. Then trace over the dotted lines to write the letters. Start at the red dot.

The letter **r** goes down, up and over.

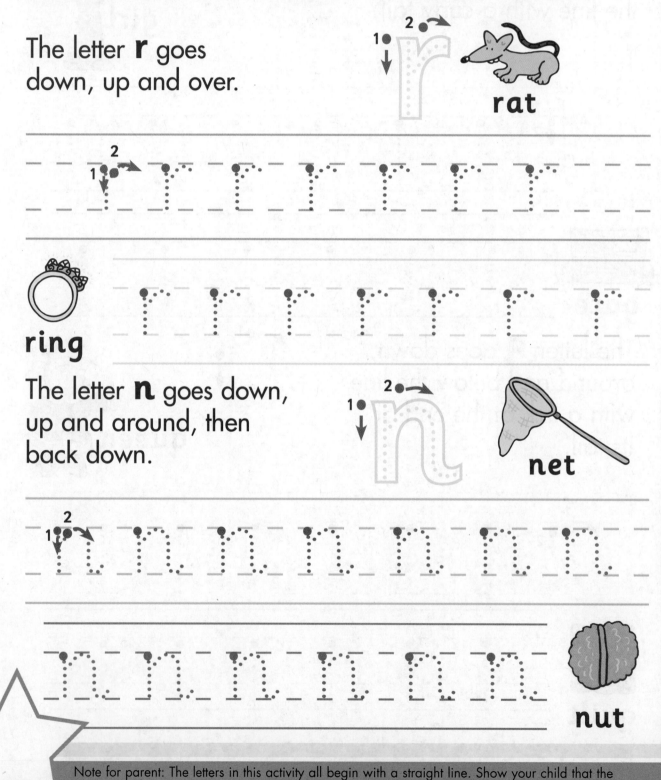

rat

ring

The letter **n** goes down, up and around, then back down.

net

nut

The letter **m** goes down, up and around, then up and around again.

mug

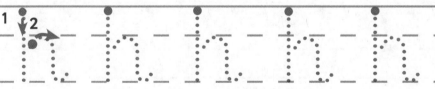

mop

The letter **h** goes down, up halfway, around and down again.

hen

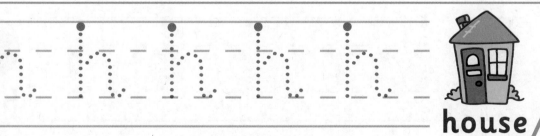

house

Writing **b**, **p** and **k**

Trace the letters with your finger. Then trace over the dotted lines to write the letters. Start at the red dot.

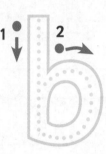

The letter **b** goes down, up halfway and round to join at the bottom.

boy

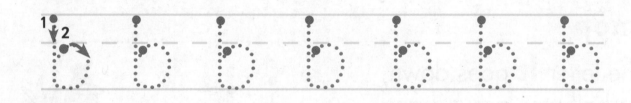

box

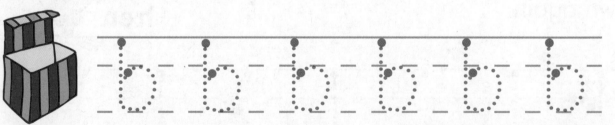

ball

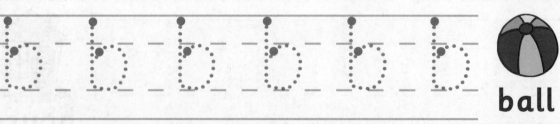

Note for parent: The letters in this activity trace back up to the middle of the stroke.

The letter **p** goes down to make a tail, up to the top and round to join halfway down.

pig

p p p p p p p

pen

p p p p p p

The letter **k** goes down, up halfway, then back round to the line before kicking out.

key

k k k k k k k

kite

k k k k k k k

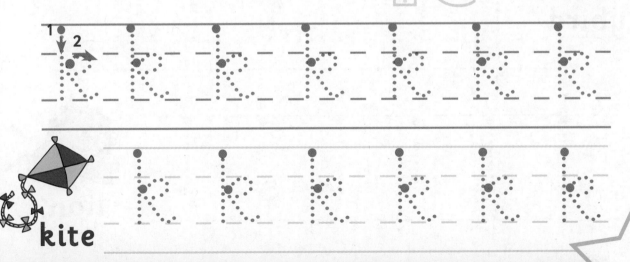

Writing l, i and j

Trace the letters with your finger. Then trace over the dotted lines to write the letters. Start at the red dot.

ladder

The letter **l** goes down.

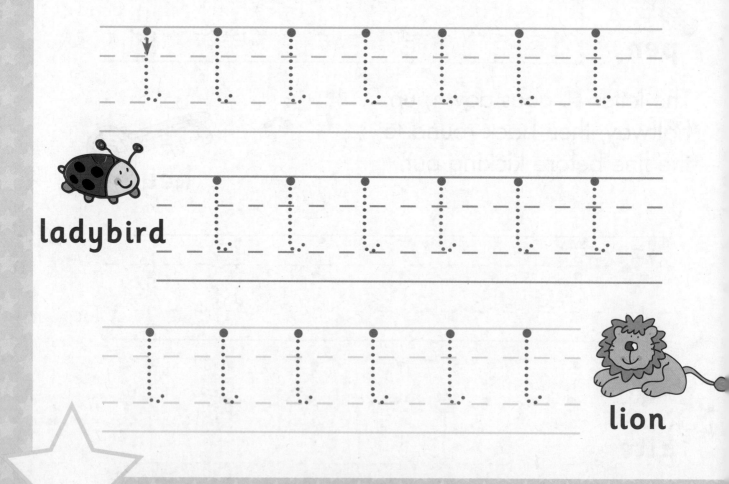

ladybird

lion

Note for parent: Help your child to position the dots above the **i** and the **j**.

The letter **i** goes down,
then add a dot above.

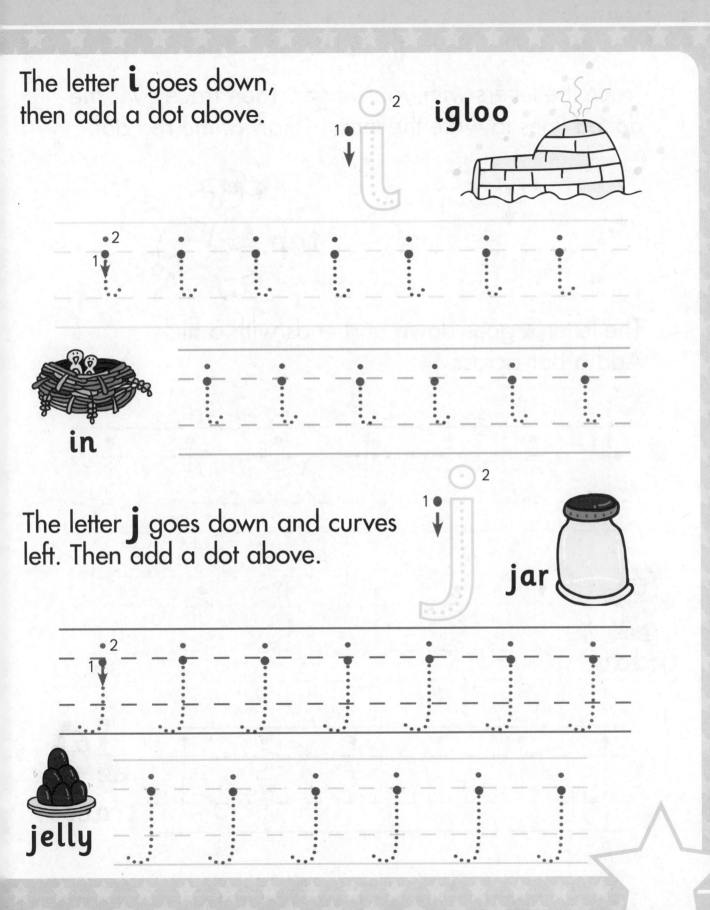

igloo

in

The letter **j** goes down and curves
left. Then add a dot above.

jar

jelly

Trace the letters with your finger. Then trace over the dotted lines to write the letters. Start at the red dot.

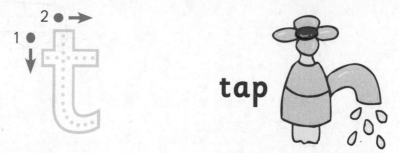

tap

The letter **t** goes down and ends with a flick. Add a bar across.

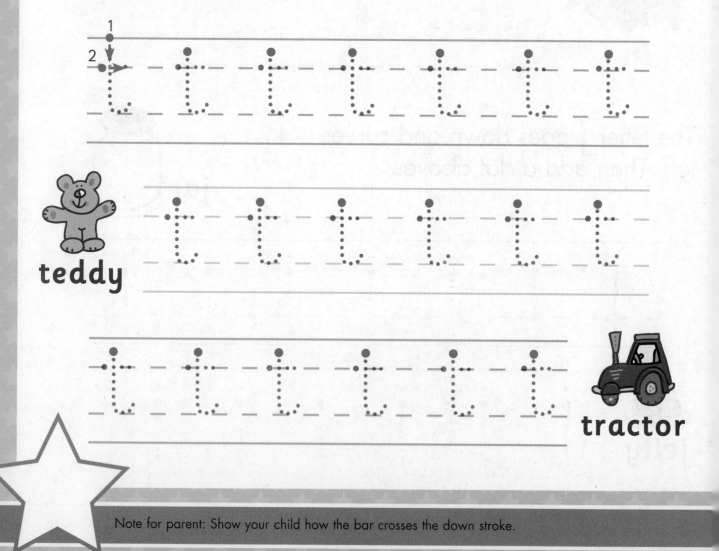

teddy

tractor

The letter **u** goes down, around, up and then down.

1 2

umbrella

up

The letter **y** goes down, around, up and then down below the line with a curly tail.

1 2

yo-yo

yellow

Note for parent: The stroke for these two letters begins in the same way.

57

Writing **v**, **w**, **x** and **z**

Trace the letters with your finger. Then trace over the dotted lines to write the letters. Start at the red dot.

The letter **v** goes down and up, making a sharp point.

van

vegetables

The letter **w** goes down, up, down and up, making two sharp points.

web

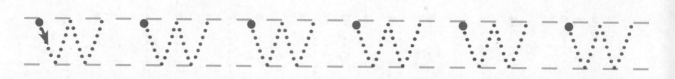

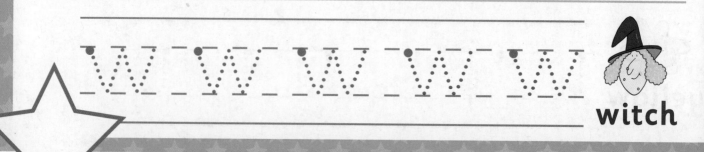
witch

The letter **X** goes down to the
right, then down to the left.

1 2

x-ray

1 2

X X X X X X X X

X X X X X X X

The letter **Z** goes across, down
to the left then across again.

Z

zebra

Z Z Z Z Z Z Z Z

Z Z Z Z Z Z Z

Writing e, f and s

Trace the letters with your finger. Then trace over the dotted lines to write the letters. Start at the red dot.

egg

The letter **e** starts in the middle, curves up and goes halfway round.

e e e e e e e

elephant e e e e e e e

e e e e e e e

Note for parent: These letters can be tricky but practice will help your child to gain confidence.

The letter **f** curves down to make a tail, then finishes with a bar across.

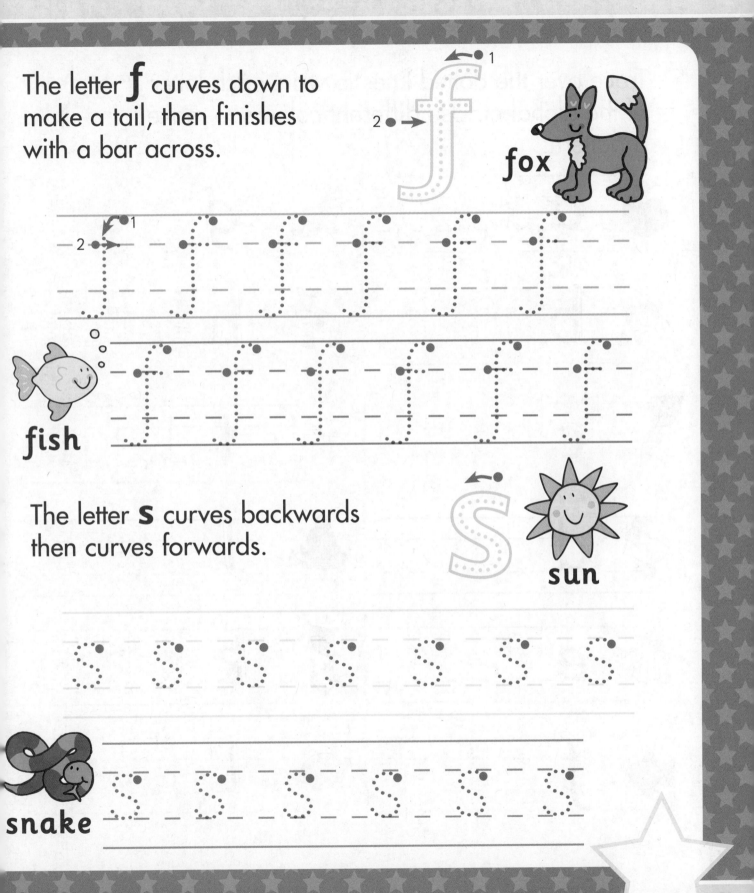

fox

fish

The letter **s** curves backwards then curves forwards.

sun

snake

The alphabet

Trace over the dotted lines to write each letter of the alphabet. Use different colours to make a pattern.

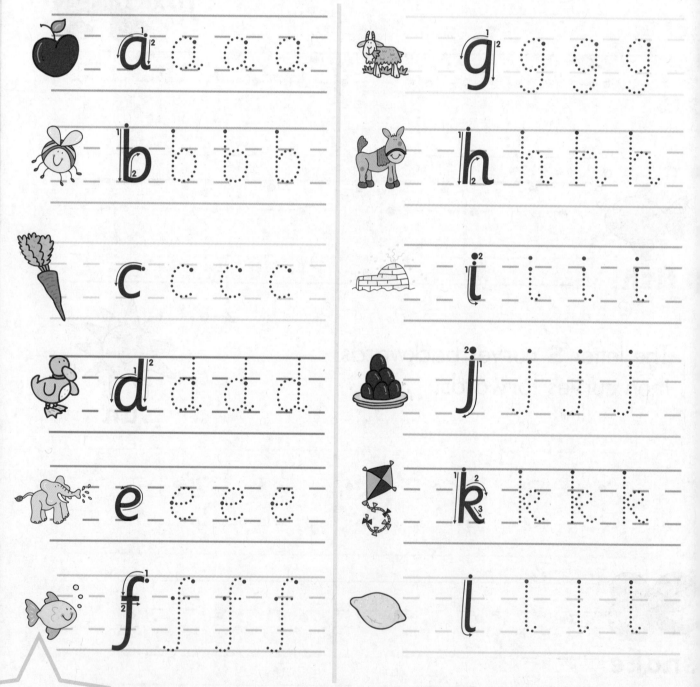

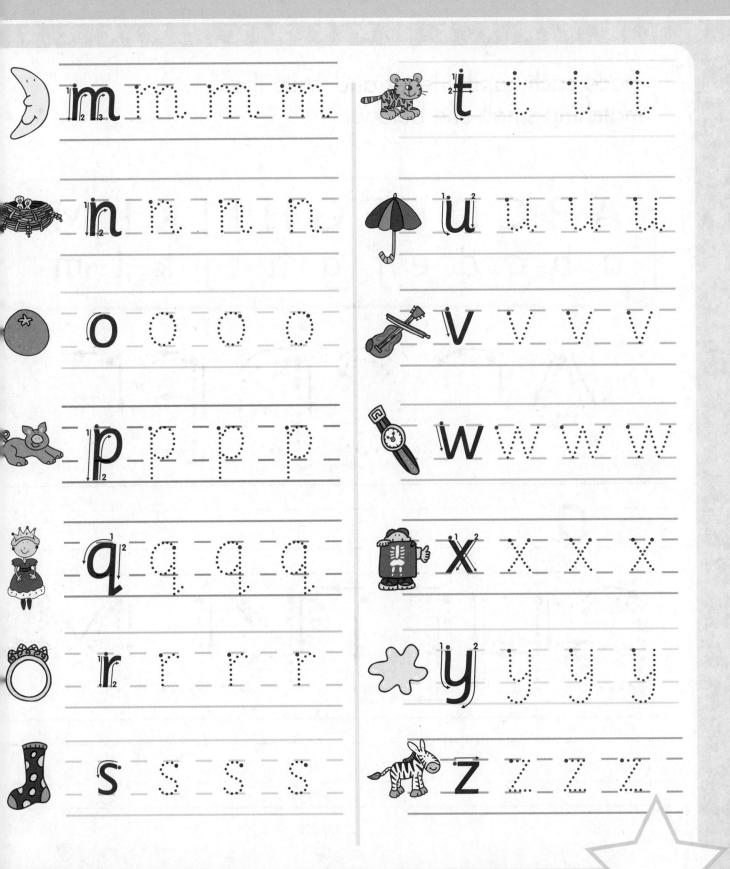

m m m m

t t t t

n n n n

u u u u

o o o o

v v v v

p p p p

w w w w

q q q q

x x x x

r r r r

y y y y

s s s s

z z z z

Writing capital letters

Trace each capital letter and write the
matching small one below.

A B C D E F G H I J K L M
a b c d e f g h i j k l m

Note for parent: This activity gives your child practice in writing all the capital and small letters.
Write the letters in the air with your finger to give further practice.

N O P Q R S T U V W X Y Z
n o p q r s t u v w x y z

Writing numbers

Trace over the dotted lines to write each number.
Start at the red dot.

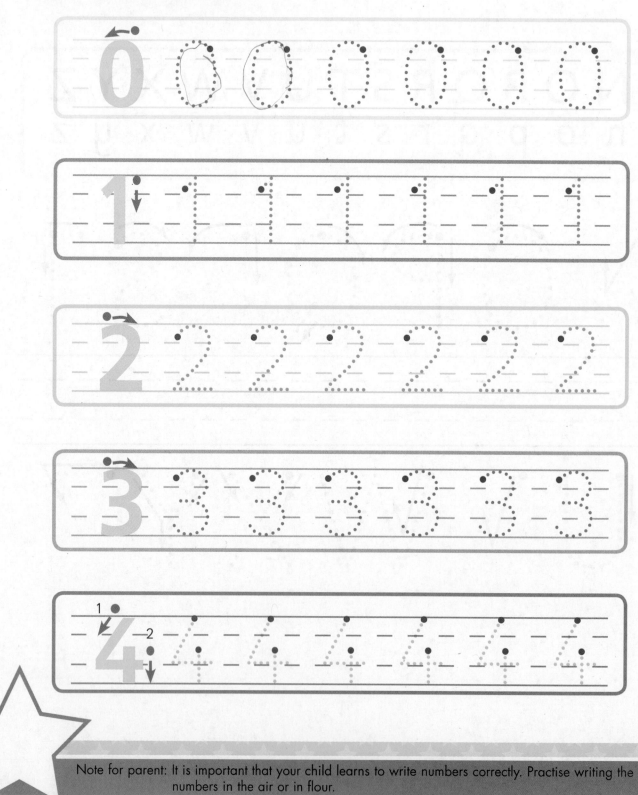

Note for parent: It is important that your child learns to write numbers correctly. Practise writing the numbers in the air or in flour.

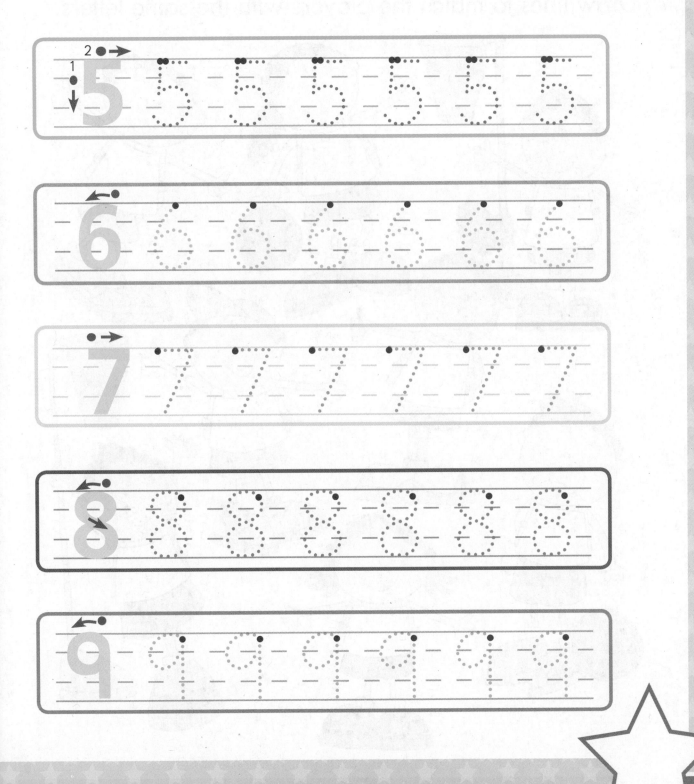

Hidden letters

Trace over the dots to write the letters on the shirts.
Draw lines to match the players with the same letters.

Note for parent: This activity helps to distinguish letters that are often confused: **m** and **n**; **u** and **v**.
Point and say each letter sound.

Fishing game

Trace the dots to write the letters. Say the sounds.
Join each fish to the boat with the same sound.

Note for parent: This activity helps your child to identify the vowels **a**, **e**, **i**, **o** and **u**.

69

Names

Write your name here, starting with a capital letter.

Draw a picture of yourself.

Note for parent: This activity helps your child to learn that all names begin with a capital letter.
Ask your child to draw your family members and write their names.

Choose names for these animals. Write the names below.

In the kitchen

Trace the words for each label.
Then write the word underneath.

cat

pan

man

dog

mug

tap

sink

Note for parent: This activity gives your child practice in writing complete words.
Encourage your child to name other things in the picture.

At school

Look at the pictures.
Trace the letters to write the words.
Read the words.

book

pencil

boy

teacher

paints

girl

A sunny day

Point to the sun, rabbit, butterfly and tree.
Trace over the letter shapes on each picture.

Note for parent: Say, "s is for sun", and so on, as your child identifies each shape.

Trace over the dotted letters.

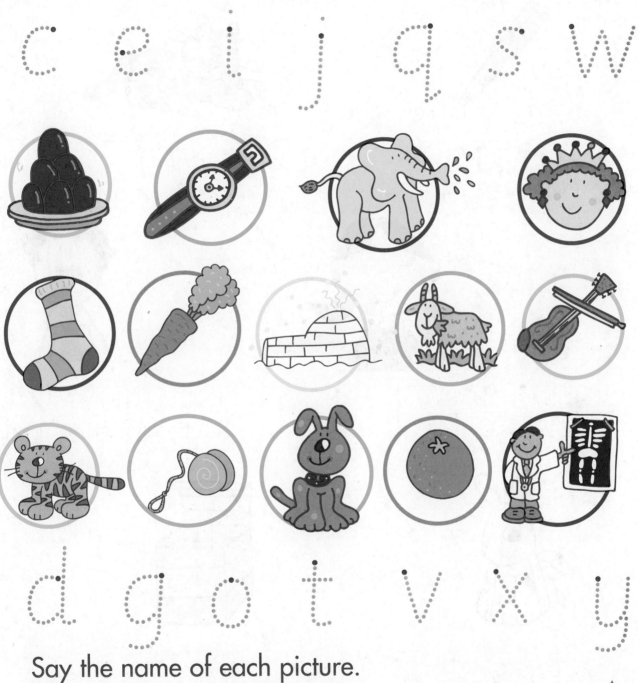

c e i j q s w

d g o t v x y

Say the name of each picture.
Draw lines to join each letter to a picture that
begins with the same letter.

Writing words

Trace over the dotted letters to write the words.

pen

cat

mum

dad

dog

box

Note for parent: Help your child to sound out each word.

bed

hat

pig

cup

bag

fox

Word puzzle

Count the letters in the words. Draw lines to join each word to the right truck.

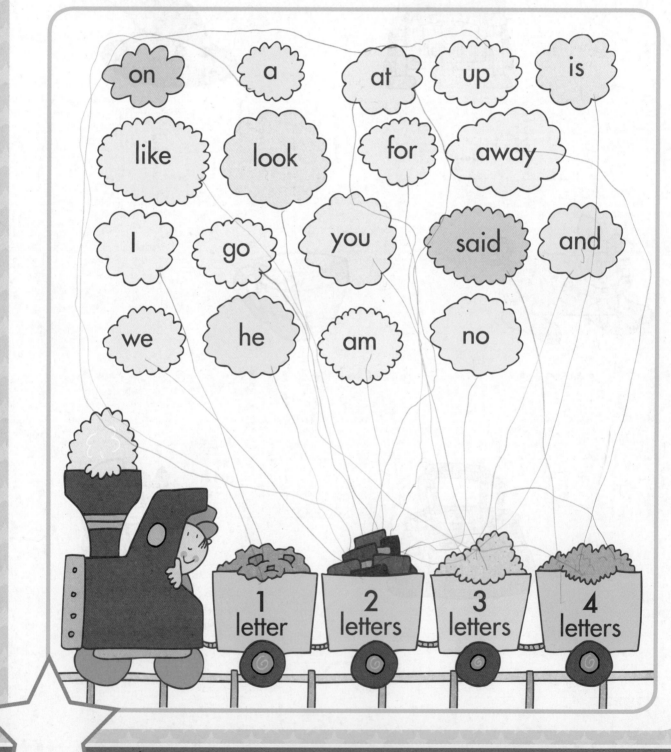

on   a   at   up   is

like   look   for   away

I   go   you   said   and

we   he   am   no

1 letter   2 letters   3 letters   4 letters

I can read

Can you read and write all the words
on this snail?

all

dog

----

big

of

----

it

she

yes

----

in

me

was

----

get

can

----

see

----

my

went

Note for parent: More practice in reading and writing high-frequency words.

Pretty patterns

Colour the clothes on the lines to make patterns.

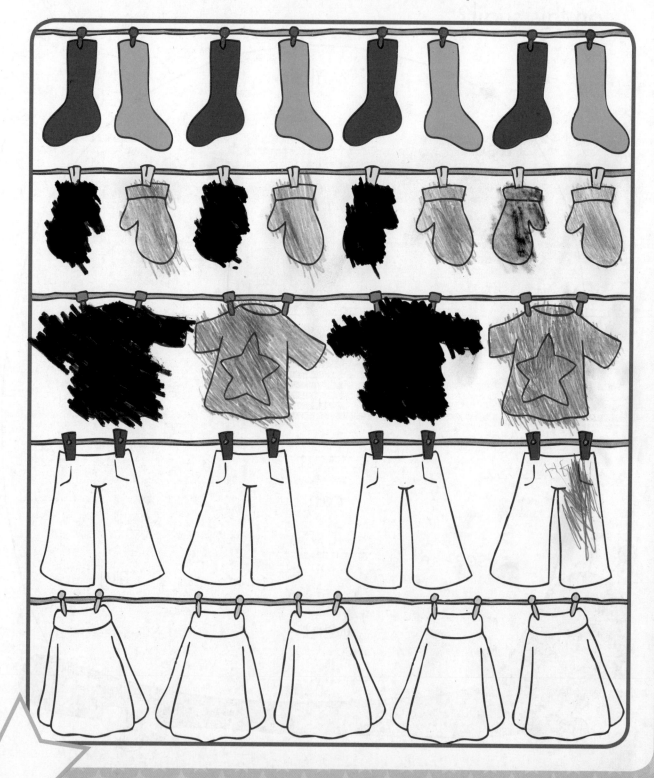

Note for parent: Use beads, toy bricks or other objects to make up sequences based on colour, size or shape.

Draw the right shapes to continue the patterns.
Colour the shapes.

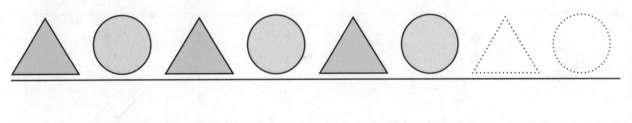

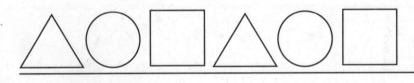

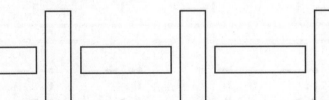

Note for parent: Encourage your child to draw shape patterns of their own on blank paper.

81

Counting to 5

Count the bees. Point to the number.
Trace it with your finger. Write the numbers.

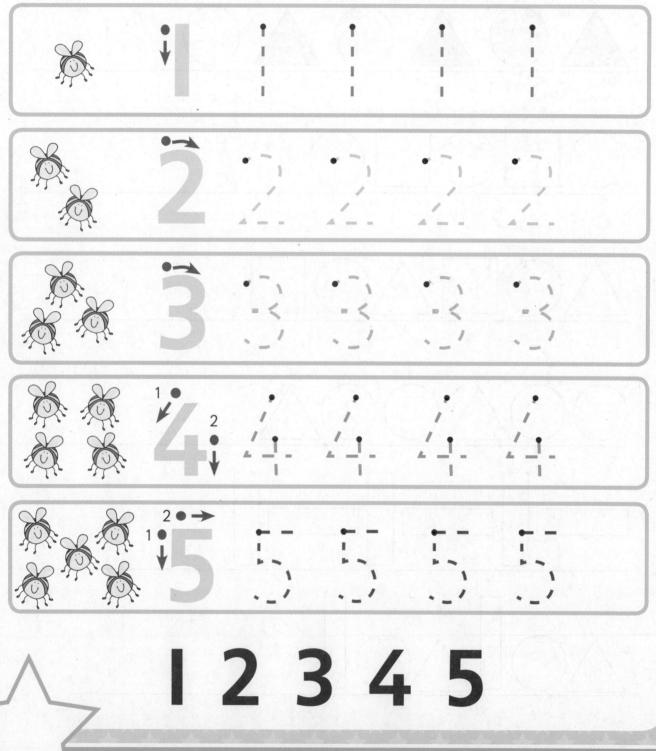

1 2 3 4 5

Note for parent: This page shows how to write the numbers 1 to 5. It helps your child with counting.
Before writing a number, your child should trace the shape with their finger.

How many?

Count the bugs. Write the answers in the boxes.

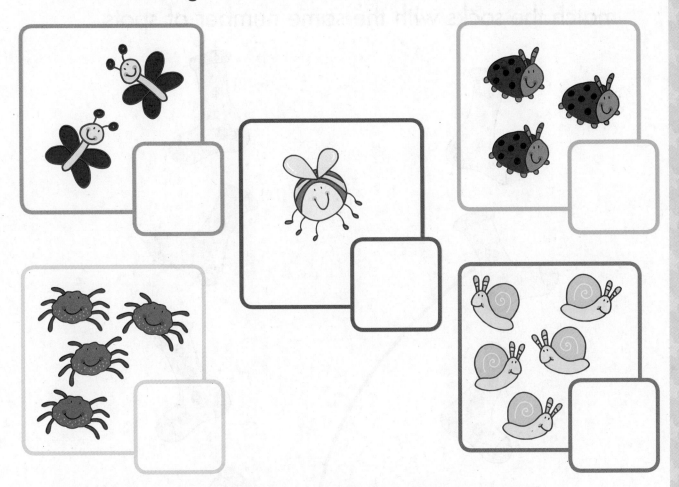

Draw five spots on the ladybird. Colour it in.

Note for parent: Have fun finding things to count in your house such as one door, two shoes, three apples, four socks and five windows.

Count the spots on each sock. Draw lines to match the socks with the same number of spots.

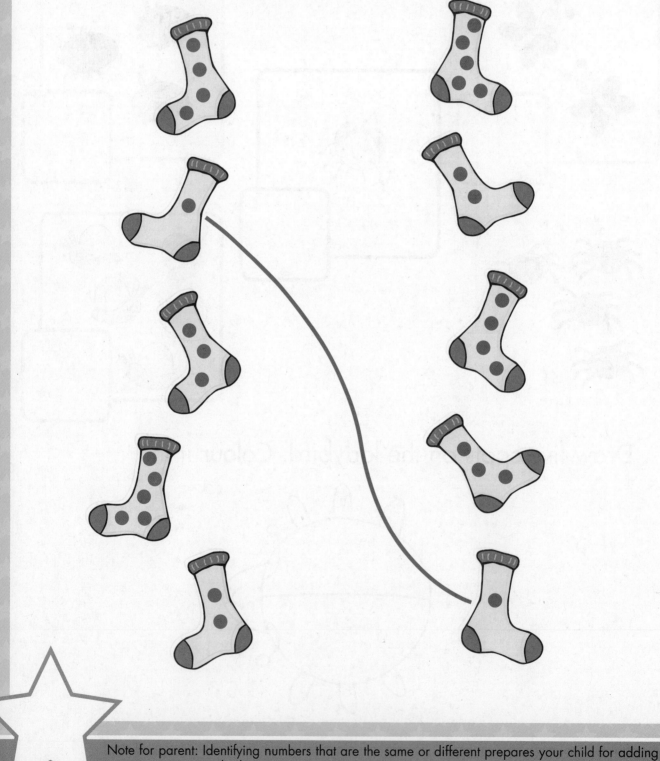

Note for parent: Identifying numbers that are the same or different prepares your child for adding and subtracting.

What's missing?

Write the missing numbers.

Draw the missing things.

Note for parent: Working out the missing objects prepares your child for adding and subtracting.

85

One more

Draw 1 more. Count the objects. How many are there altogether? Write the numbers in the boxes.

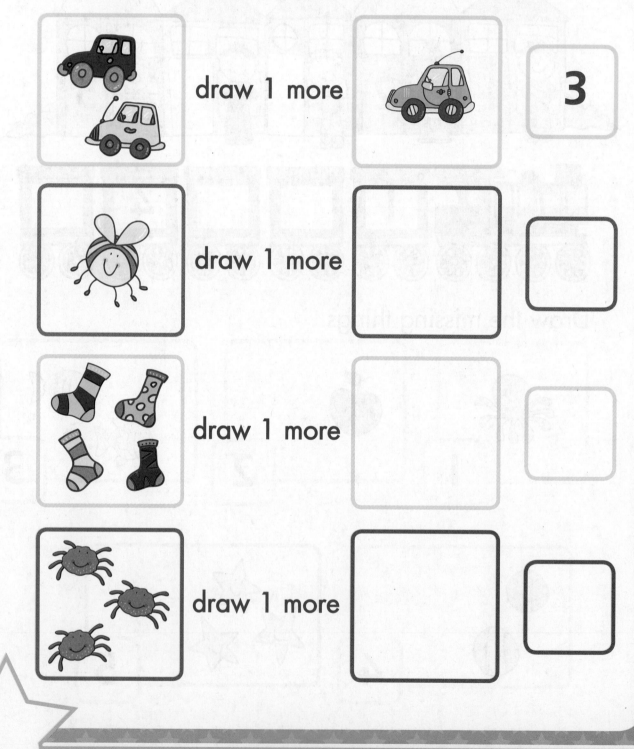

draw 1 more

3

draw 1 more

draw 1 more

draw 1 more

Note for parent: This page prepares your child for adding. Ask "How many altogether?" "Three spiders and one more spider makes four spiders altogether."

Circle the correct answers.

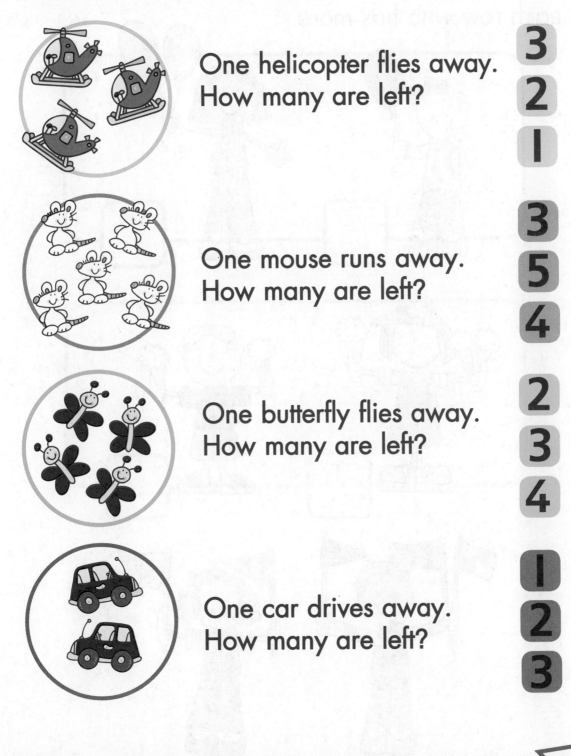

One helicopter flies away.
How many are left?

3
2
1

One mouse runs away.
How many are left?

3
5
4

One butterfly flies away.
How many are left?

2
3
4

One car drives away.
How many are left?

1
2
3

Note for parent: This page prepares your child for subtracting or taking away. Play a game: show five fingers, hide one finger to show 'one less'. How many fingers are left?

Look at the pictures. Put a tick by the person in each row who has more.

Note for parent: This activity gives more practice in counting from one to three.

The same or more?

Join each rabbit to a hole. Are there more rabbits or more holes? Tick the correct box.

more rabbits ☐   more holes ☐

Join each kennel to a dog. Are there more dogs or more kennels? Tick the correct box.

more kennels ☐   more dogs ☐

Note for parent: Matching objects one by one shows if the numbers are the same or different.

Hidden numbers

There are 9 ducks in each line, but some are hidden. Write down how many are hidden.

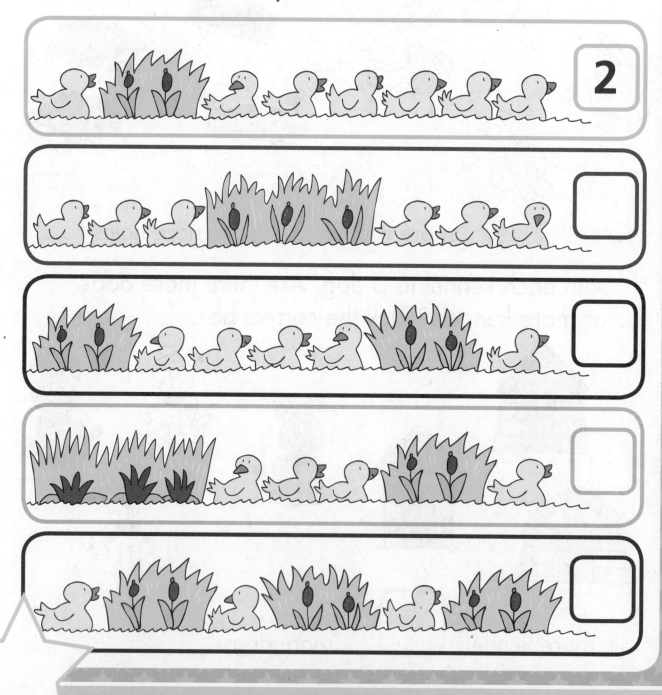

Note for parent: These are good activities to do with real toys. Make them fun!

Count the different crayons. How many are there in each jar? Write down the totals.

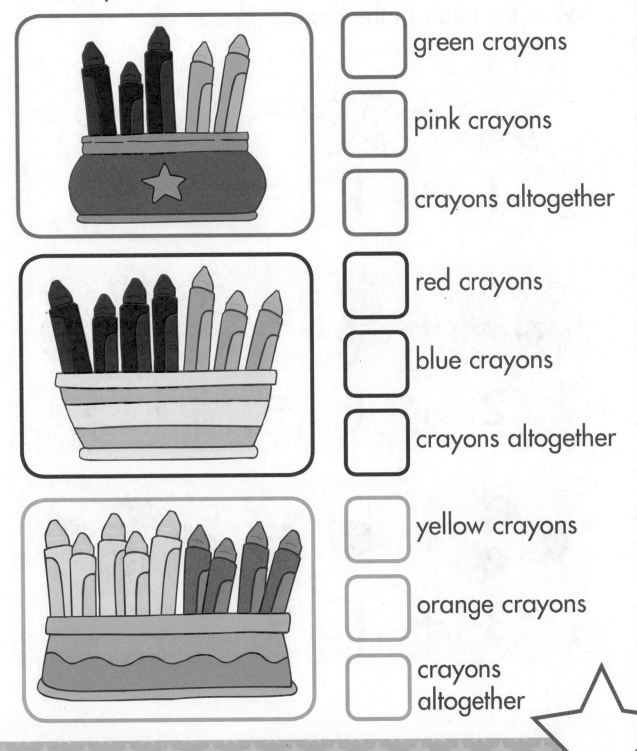

☐ green crayons

☐ pink crayons

☐ crayons altogether

☐ red crayons

☐ blue crayons

☐ crayons altogether

☐ yellow crayons

☐ orange crayons

☐ crayons altogether

Add one

Point to each picture and count the objects.
Say the numbers out loud.
Write the totals in the boxes.

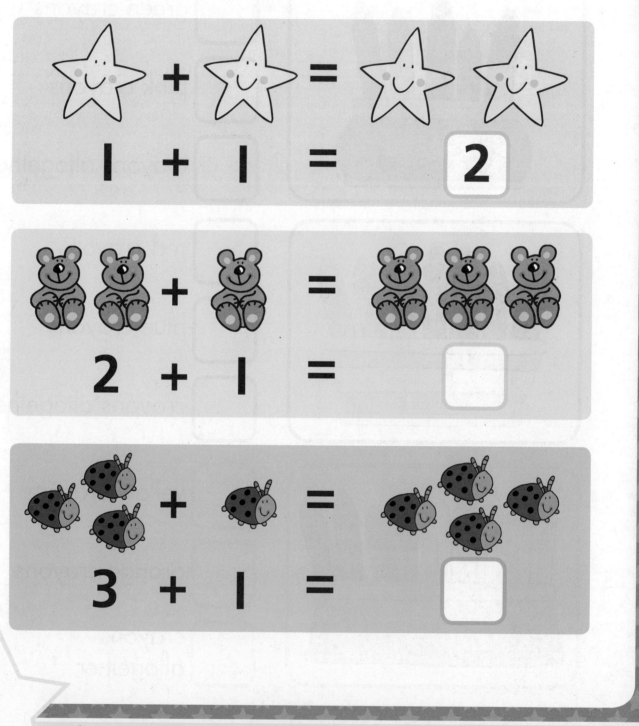

$1 + 1 = 2$

$2 + 1 = $

$3 + 1 = $

Note for parent: Counting on shows that the last number counted gives the total. Hold up two fingers, then hold up one more. Two fingers add one finger makes (one, two,) three fingers altogether.

Take away one

Count the animals. Take one away.
How many are left?
Write in the missing numbers.

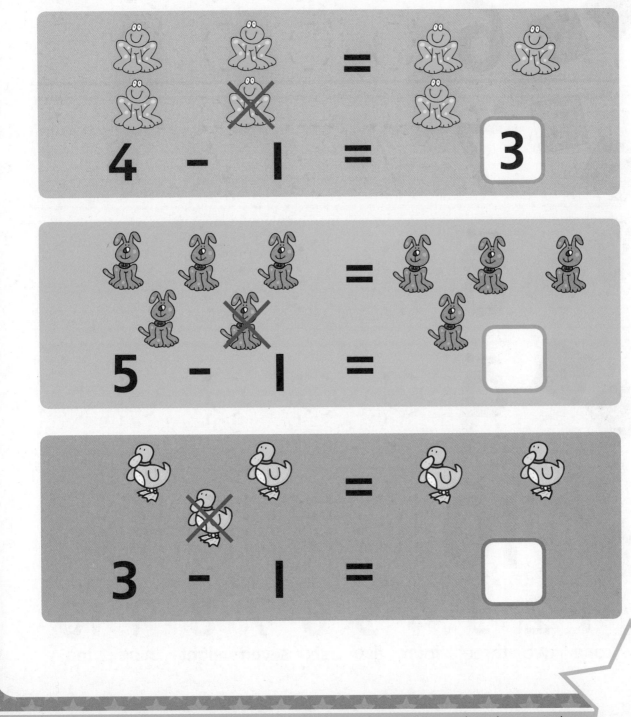

$$4 - 1 = 3$$

$$5 - 1 = \boxed{}$$

$$3 - 1 = \boxed{}$$

Numbers up to 10

Count the spots on the dice. Point to the numbers.
Trace them with your finger. Write the numbers.

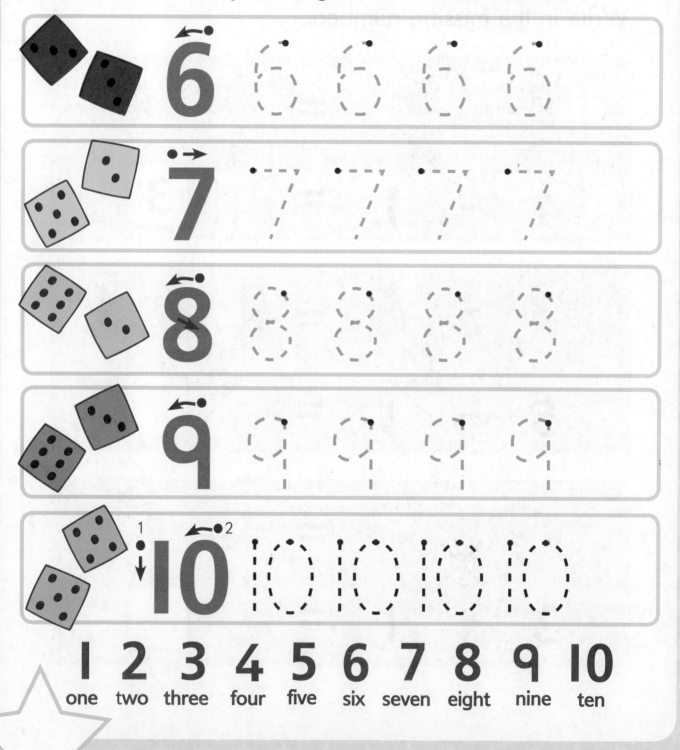

1	2	3	4	5	6	7	8	9	10
one	two	three	four	five	six	seven	eight	nine	ten

Note for parent: It is important that your child learns to write numbers correctly.

Count the number of each thing and write the answers in the boxes.

ducklings

horse

flowers

bees

trees

pigs

sunflowers

cows

wheels

sheep

Colour the picture.

Note for parent: This activity gives your child practice in counting up to ten. Ask your child to guess (estimate) how many of each thing first. Count to see how close they are.

Ordering numbers

Write in the missing numbers.

(1)( )(3)(4)(5)(6)( )( )(9)(10)

Note for parent: This activity gives your child practice in counting forwards and backwards. Play countdown games. Who will be first to finish? 5, 4, 3, 2, 1, go!

Counting in 2s

Write the totals in the boxes.
There are two spots altogether.

2

Draw two arms on each teddy.
How many arms altogether?

Draw two legs on each duck.
How many legs altogether?

Draw two ears on each cat.
How many ears altogether?

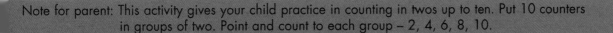

Note for parent: This activity gives your child practice in counting in twos up to ten. Put 10 counters in groups of two. Point and count to each group – 2, 4, 6, 8, 10.

Take away 4

Cross out four animals from each set.
Write how many are left.

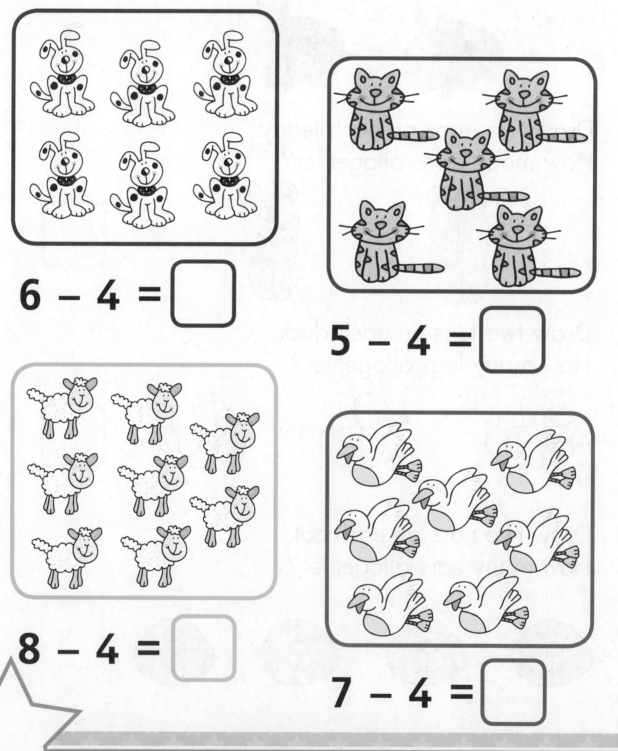

6 – 4 =

5 – 4 =

8 – 4 =

7 – 4 =

Note for parent: These activities will help your child to recognize the symbol for subtraction.

Pop the balloons

Pop four balloons from each bunch by crossing them out. Write how many are left.

9 – 4 = ☐

10 – 4 = ☐

4 – 4 = ☐

Note for parent: Your child should begin to use the zero symbol, 0, for 'none' or 'nothing'.

Adding numbers

Look at the sums. They use a number track to find the answers. Write in the answers.

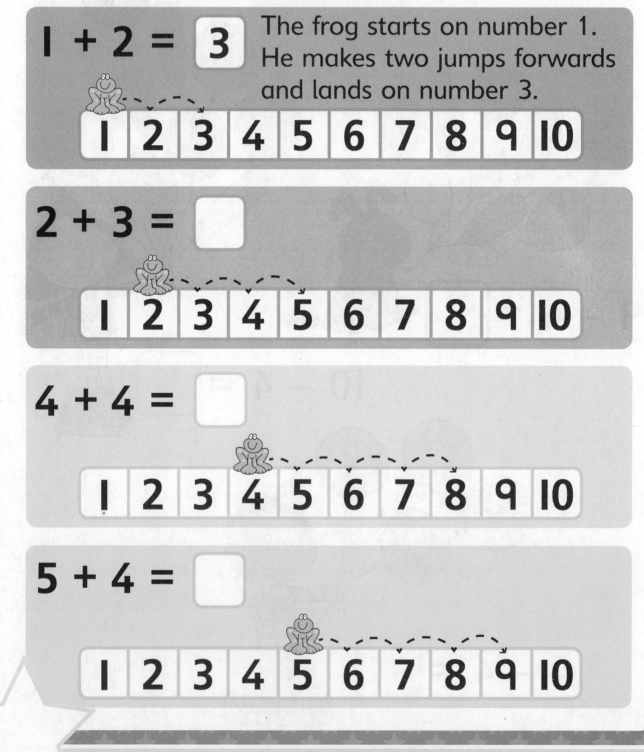

1 + 2 = 3

The frog starts on number 1. He makes two jumps forwards and lands on number 3.

1 2 3 4 5 6 7 8 9 10

2 + 3 =

1 2 3 4 5 6 7 8 9 10

4 + 4 =

1 2 3 4 5 6 7 8 9 10

5 + 4 =

1 2 3 4 5 6 7 8 9 10

Note for parent: This activity shows your child how to use a number track to add. Start at a number and add on another number without beginning from 1 each time.

Taking away

Look at the sums. They use a number track to find the answers. Write in the answers.

3 – 2 = 1

The frog starts on number 3. He makes two jumps backwards and lands on number 1.

1 2 3 4 5 6 7 8 9 10

5 – 2 = ▢

1 2 3 4 5 6 7 8 9 10

7 – 4 = ▢

1 2 3 4 5 6 7 8 9 10

10 – 3 = ▢

1 2 3 4 5 6 7 8 9 10

Note for parent: This activity shows how to take away (subtract) using a number track. Explain that taking something away means you end up with less.

Numbers up to 20

Count the spots on the dice. Point to the numbers.
Trace them with your finger. Write the numbers.

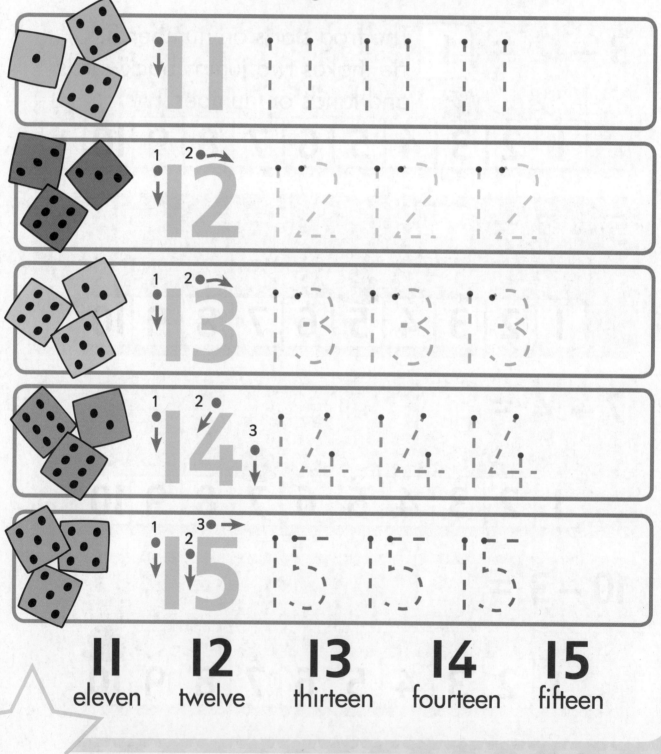

11 eleven **12** twelve **13** thirteen **14** fourteen **15** fifteen

Note for parent: These pages will give your child practice in counting up to twenty.
It is important that your child learns to write numbers correctly.

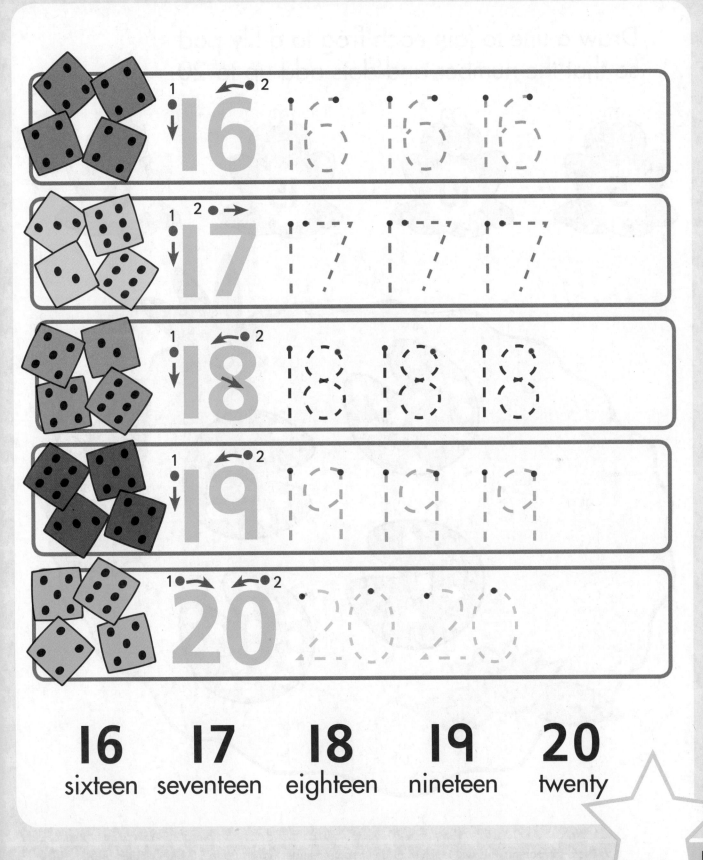

16 sixteen **17** seventeen **18** eighteen **19** nineteen **20** twenty

Hop up to 20

Draw a line to join each frog to a lily pad so that the number and dots add up to 20.

 **5**  **10**  **15**  **0**

Note for parent: This will teach your child some number bonds up to 20, in multiples of 5. These simple addition facts make adding and multiplying much easier.

How many marbles in each jar? Make a guess.
Count to see if you are right. Draw more marbles
in each jar to make 20.

guess

count

guess

count

guess

count

guess

count

Note for parent: This activity gives practice in estimating. Ask questions such as "Do you think there are more than 10?" "Do you think there are less than 20?"

105

Money

How much? Add up the money in each purse.

total = ☐

total = ☐

total = ☐

total = ☐

Circle the items you would buy. They must add up to 20.

5 pencil

10 apple

5 banana

20 cake

2 marble

10 ice cream

Note for parent: This activity gives additional practice in adding up to 20. Use real coins to match the money in each purse – this will help your child to count out and add them up.

Time

Fill in the missing numbers.

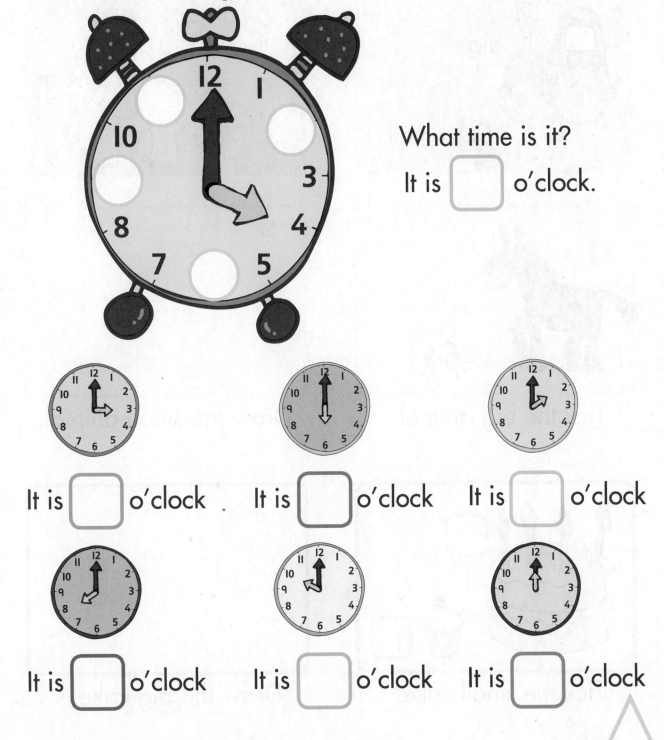

What time is it?

It is ☐ o'clock.

It is ☐ o'clock

It is ☐ o'clock

It is ☐ o'clock

It is ☐ o'clock

It is ☐ o'clock

It is ☐ o'clock

Note for parent: Time can be a tricky concept for children. Encourage your child to read the clock at set times each day, such as breakfast at 8 o'clock, lunch at 12 o'clock, etc.

107

Big and small

big

small

small

big

Tick the big animal.

Draw the small animal.

Tick the small cake.

Draw the big cake.

Note for parent: This activity helps your child to compare sizes. Use words such as small, smaller, smallest, big, bigger, biggest.

Heavy and light

heavy   light

light   heavy

Tick the heavy animal.

Draw the heavy animal.

Tick the light object.

Draw the light object.

Note for parent: This activity helps your child to compare different weights. Use words such as light, lighter, lightest, heavy, heavier, heaviest.

109

Longer or shorter?

Look at this pencil.

Find all the pencils that are longer than this one. Circle them.

What colour is the longest pencil? What colour is the shortest pencil?

Note for parent: This activity helps your child to compare objects. Ask them to explain how they found the answer.

Taller or shorter?

Draw a taller tree.   Draw a shorter tree.

Draw a shorter house.   Draw a taller house.

Draw a circle around the shortest child.

Note for parent: This activity gives your child practice in identifying short and tall. Use words such as short, shorter, shortest, tall, taller, tallest.

III

Tall, short and long

tall

long

short

Circle the shortest animal.

Circle the tallest house.

Draw a scarf longer than this one.

Note for parent: Measure the height of your child and other family members. Compare them using words such as tall, taller, tallest, short, shorter, shortest.

Circle the cake with more candles.

Circle the ladybird with less spots.

Which boxes have more in them? Tick the one you think has more. Then count to see if you are right.

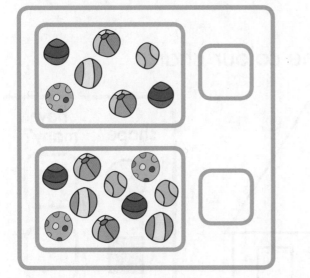

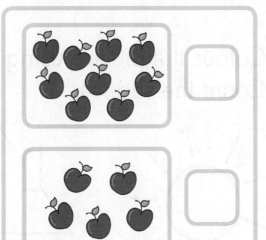

Draw a nest with more birds in it than this one.

Note for parent: This activity helps your child to understand estimating and the terms 'more' and 'less'.

Shapes

Trace over the dotted shapes. Draw them below.
Then colour them in.

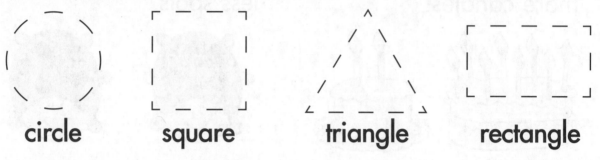

circle   square   triangle   rectangle

Colour the picture using the colour chart.
Count the shapes.

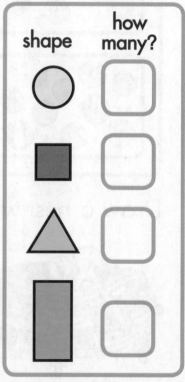

shape	how many?
circle	
square	
triangle	
rectangle	

Note for parent: This activity helps your child to recognize shapes and colours. Talk about the number of sides each shape has and how rectangles differ from squares.

Patterns

Finish the patterns.

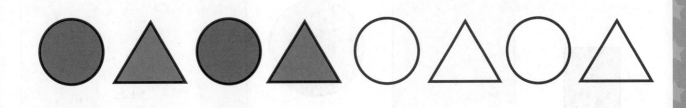

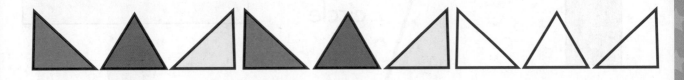

Make up your own pattern using shapes.

Note for parent: Recognizing patterns in shapes helps your child with reasoning and problem solving. Make simple repeating patterns with beads or buttons.

Flat shapes

Join each shape to its name.

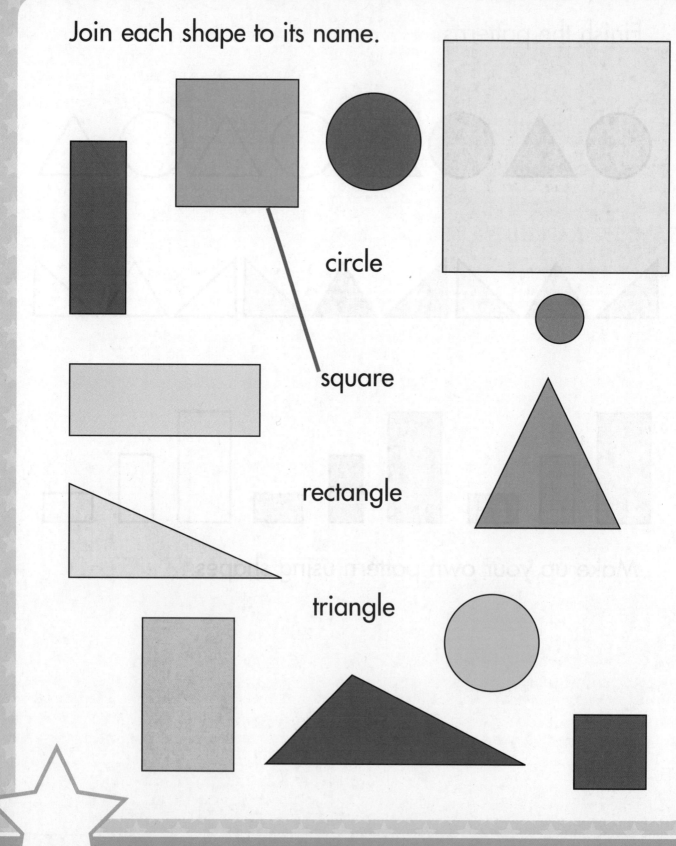

circle

square

rectangle

triangle

Note for parent: Look for circles, squares, rectangles and triangles in and around the home.

Shapes and sizes

Tick the largest shape in each box.

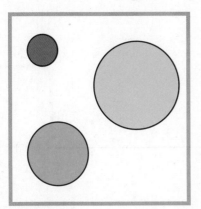 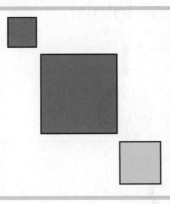 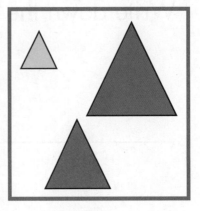

Tick the smallest shape in each box.

Number these shapes in order of size, biggest first.

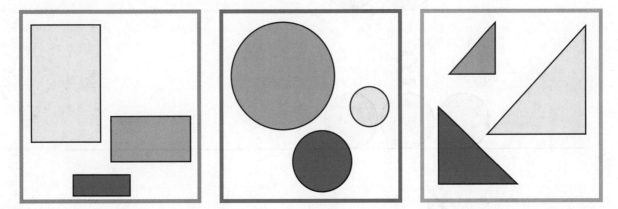

Doubles

Double the number of circles in each row.
Write down the new totals.

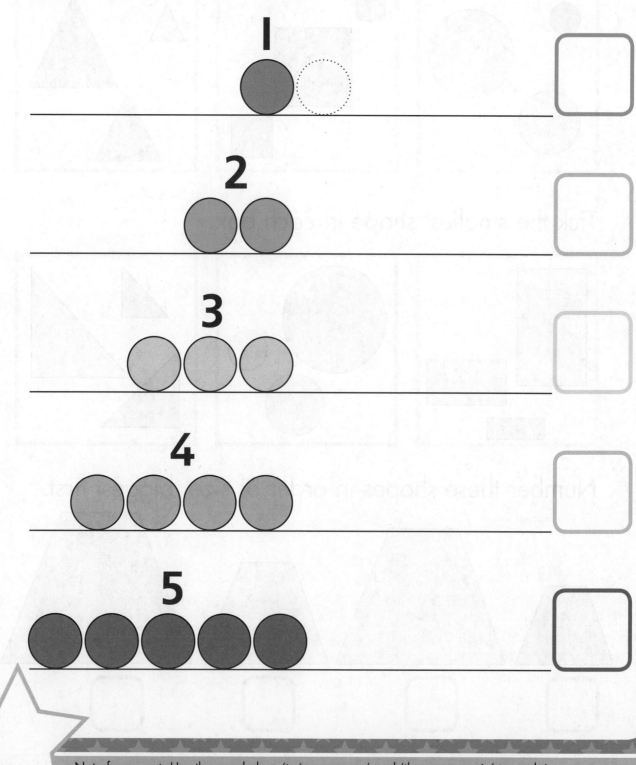

1

2

3

4

5

Note for parent: Use the vocabulary 'twice as many' and 'the same again' to explain the meaning of doubling.

Full, empty or half-full?

Some of these bottles and jars are full. Some are empty. Some are half-full. Draw lines to the right labels.

full   empty   half-full

Doubles

Copy the dots in the boxes to make doubles.
Count how many dots altogether. Write the answers
in the boxes.

double 3 makes   **6**

double 4 makes   8

double 5 makes   10

double 6 makes   12

Add balloons to double the number that each
clown holds.

Note for parent: This activity gives practice in understanding doubles.

Colour half of the spots on each ladybird.

Share the pizza equally between the two children.
Draw a line to cut the pizza in half.

Note for parent: This activity gives practice in understanding halves.

121

More halves

Draw the missing half of each thing.

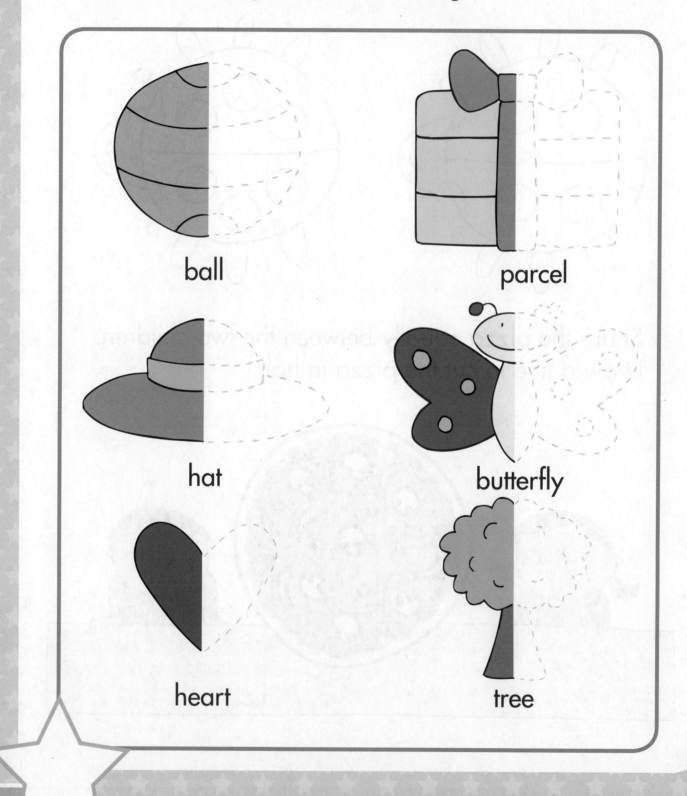

ball

parcel

hat

butterfly

heart

tree

Share it out

Draw lines to cut each thing in half. Make sure you are fair!

Are the sweets shared fairly? Put a tick or a cross.

Answers

Pages 6–7

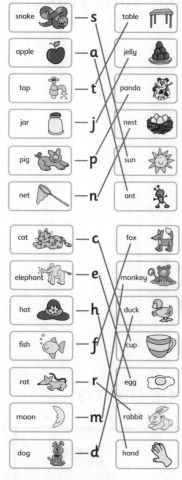

snake — s
apple — a
tap — t
jar — j
pig — p
net — n

table
jelly
panda
nest
sun
ant

cat — c
elephant — e
hat — h
fish — f
rat — r
moon — m
dog — d

fox
monkey
duck
cup
egg
rabbit
hand

Pages 8–9

goat   duck   gate

octopus   ostrich   van

umbrella   upside-down   watch

lion   arrow   lemon

fish   duck   fox

Page 10

juggler   elephant   jelly

zebra   zip   teddy

window   lion   witch

violin   van   butterfly

yo-yo   apple   yellow

cow   cap   rocket

mouse   car   bat   key

boat   frog   house   star

cat   tree   coat   dog

Page 11

To Mr Fox

To Miss Bee

To Mrs Bear

To Mr Rat

Page 12

tap
bun
pen
mat
bug
van

C ap
S un
h en
r at
m ug
f an

Page 13

Or: slide, snail, cloud, butterfly, boy

f   s   c   b

Page 15

b	x	e	s	j	k
e	y	t	p	a	n
d	a	v	n	a	b
z	m	u	m	q	h
c	f	n	l	u	i
a	o	g	p	a	t
t	r	n	e	t	a
d	a	d	w	d	p

Page 16

p **b**   m **n**   p **d**

g **k**   t **c**   b **d**

x **n**   m **k**   n **m**

Answers

Page 17
cars, bees, eggs, rugs

Page 18
small, full, new, off

Page 20

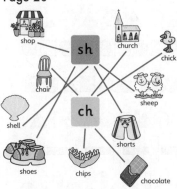

Page 21

```
        t
        h
t       u       t
t h i m b l      h
h       b        e
r                r
o       t        m
n       h i n e  o
e                m
        t h r e  e
                 t
                 e
                 r
```

Page 22
pin, bus, log, web, cat, net

Page 23

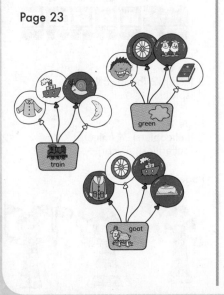

Page 24

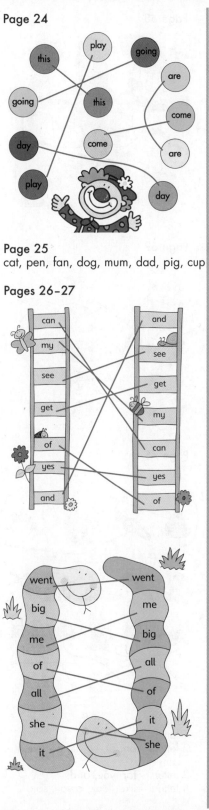

Page 25
cat, pen, fan, dog, mum, dad, pig, cup

Pages 26–27

Page 28

and	back	said	she
the	went	look	they
look	they	and	went
said	she	the	back

A boy and a girl went to the pet shop.
The girl said she liked the puppy.
They went back to look at the puppy.

Page 29

mother
father
grandad
octopus
window
crayon

Page 30

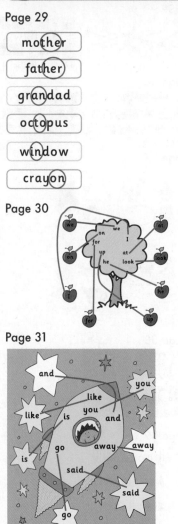

Page 31

Page 32
house, roof, window, door, garage

Answers

Page 33
This is my <u>cat</u>.
It <u>is</u> white.
It has <u>a</u> long tail.
This is a <u>dog</u>.
It <u>can</u> bark.
It is <u>big</u>.

Page 34
The coat is on the back of the <u>door</u>.
The <u>net</u> is under the bed.
The <u>dinosaur</u> is on the bed.
The chair is near the <u>desk</u>.

Page 35
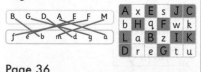

Page 36

Who caught the fish?	Dan	Poppy	Mia
Who caught the crab?	Poppy	Dan	Ali
What did Dan catch?	key	crab	ring

Page 37

Page 38

Page 39
they some all
do was little
said like
have what when

Page 68

Page 69
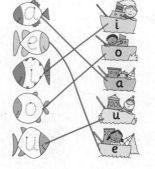

Page 75
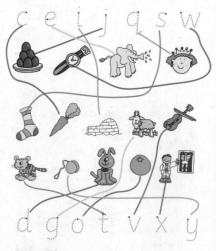

Page 78
1 letter – a, I
2 letters – on, at, up, is, go, we, he, am, no
3 letters – for, you, and,
4 letters – like, look, away, said

Page 83
2 (butterflies), 1 (bee),
3 (ladybirds), 4 (spiders),
5 (snails)

Page 81
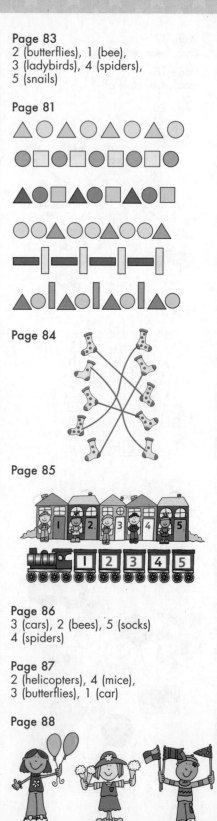

Page 84

Page 85

Page 86
3 (cars), 2 (bees), 5 (socks)
4 (spiders)

Page 87
2 (helicopters), 4 (mice),
3 (butterflies), 1 (car)

Page 88

Answers

Page 89
more holes ✓   more dogs ✓

Page 90
line 2: 3 are hidden
line 3: 4 are hidden
line 4: 5 are hidden
line 5: 6 are hidden

Page 91
2 green crayons, 3 pink crayons,
5 crayons altogether
4 red crayons, 3 blue crayons,
7 crayons altogether
5 yellow crayons, 4 orange crayons,
9 crayons altogether

Page 92
3 (teddies), 4 (ladybirds)

Page 93
4 (dogs), 2 (ducks)

Page 95
8 (ducklings), 1 (horse),
10 (flowers), 9 (bees), 4 (trees),
5 (pigs), 7 (sunflowers), 2 (cows),
3 (wheels), 6 (sheep)

Page 96

Page 97
4 (teddy arms), 6 (duck legs),
8 (cat ears)

Page 98
6 − 4 = 2
5 − 4 = 1
8 − 4 = 4
7 − 4 = 3

Page 99
9 − 4 = 5
10 − 4 = 6
4 − 4 = 0

Page 100
2 + 3 = 5, 4 + 4 = 8
5 + 4 = 9

Page 101
5 − 2 = 3, 7 − 4 = 3
10 − 3 = 7

Page 104

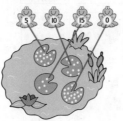

Page 105

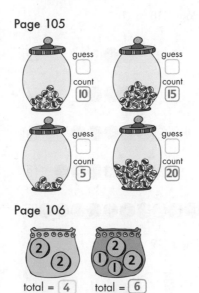

Page 106

Page 107

Page 108

Page 109

Page 110

The longest pencil is purple.
The shortest pencil is red.

Page 111

Page 112

Answers

Page 113

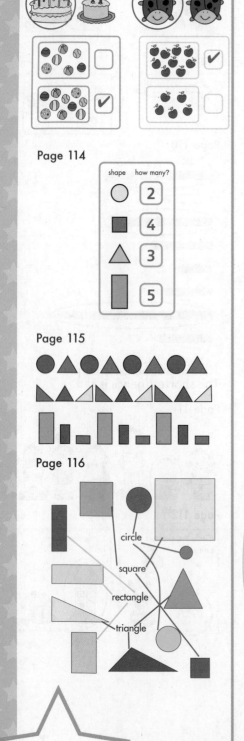

Page 114

shape	how many?
○	2
■	4
△	3
▮	5

Page 115

Page 116

circle

square

rectangle

triangle

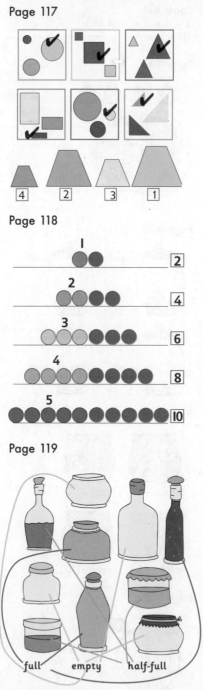

Page 117

4	2	3	1

Page 118

1   2

2   4

3   6

4   8

5   10

Page 119

full   empty   half-full

Page 120
Double 4 makes 8
Double 5 makes 10
Double 6 makes 12

Page 121

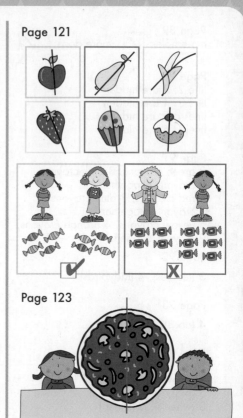

Page 123